A handbook of softwoods

London, Her Majesty's Stationery Office

This *title* was originally issued by the Department of Scientific and Industrial Research which is now dissolved and this new edition is issued by the Department of the Environment.

Full details of all new BRE publications are published quarterly in BRE NEWS.
Requests for BRE NEWS or placing on the mailing list should be addressed to:
Distribution Unit
Application Services Division
Building Research Station
Garston, Watford WD2 7JR.

ISBN 0 11 470563 1

Preface

The first *Handbook of Empire Timbers*, which contained information on species both home-grown and from the Commonwealth and Empire countries, was issued by the Empire Marketing Board in 1932. By 1939 this book was almost out of print and, as in the meantime the Laboratory had investigated a considerable number of species, it was replaced by two volumes, one on oversea[1] and one on home-grown[2] timbers.

These two handbooks, revised at intervals, have served a useful purpose during the war and post-war periods, but the time has arrived for a revision and enlargement in scope of the earlier books.

It has been decided that it would be more useful to group the hardwoods and the softwoods in separate volumes, and to bring together in each volume both the home-grown and imported timbers.

The volume on hardwoods has been published[3].

The present volume on softwoods contains up-to-date information on the softwood species formerly dealt with in both the earlier volumes and also data on a number of additional species. Altogether the book gives a full description of 49 timbers and another six are described briefly.

F Y Henderson
Director of Forest Products Research

Forest Products Research Laboratory
Princes Risborough
Aylesbury, Bucks.

December 1956

[1] *A Handbook of Empire Timbers* (Revised Edition 1945), H.M. Stationery Office.
[2] *A Handbook of Home-grown Timbers* (Revised Edition 1941), H.M. Stationery Office.
[3] *A Handbook of Hardwoods* (1956), H.M. Stationery Office.

Contents

Introduction

Much of the technical information contained in this volume has been derived from tests at the Building Research Establishment, Princes Risborough Laboratory, or at similar research institutions. Laboratory tests are necessarily on a limited amount of timber. Although care is taken to obtain as nearly as possible average material for test, it should be understood that the properties of any timber are liable to considerable variation according to conditions of growth. Paragraphs concerned with the description of the trees and the natural distribution of the species have necessarily been based largely on published information. Information concerning uses has been compiled from many sources. Though care has been taken to obtain confirmatory evidence, wherever possible, of all information from outside sources, the Laboratory cannot vouch for its absolute accuracy. In cases of doubt, however, the policy has been to err on the side of caution.

Special attention is drawn to the following paragraphs.

The weights of timbers

The weight of a piece of wood depends on several factors. It will obviously vary with the amount of water it contains. For this reason it is important that, when the weight of a timber is stated, the moisture content at which the weight determination was made should be cited.

In the general description of each timber, the weights given for 'green' timber have been obtained, whenever possible, from material recently converted from the log, and the average moisture content of the wood, where known, is stated in brackets. The weights of the timbers when seasoned refer to a moisture content of 12 per cent. The weight of a timber at any other moisture content within the range of, say, 5 per cent and 25 per cent can be estimated with fair accuracy by adding or subtracting 0·5 per cent of the given weight for each 1 per cent moisture content above or below 12 per cent.

In all species a considerable variation in weight is found to occur apart from that arising from differences in the amount of contained moisture. The average weights given in the text are only approximate and where sufficient information is available to justify quoting a range, this has been done.

Shrinkage and movement

Shrinkage measurements in the tangential and radial directions, which were obtained in the kiln drying (from the green state to a moisture content of 12 per cent) of material sawn through and through, are expressed in percentages.

The term 'movement' is used in referring to the dimensional changes that take place when seasoned timber is subjected to changes in atmospheric conditions. To determine the movement values quoted, test samples were conditioned first in air at 90 per cent humidity, and then in air at 60 per cent humidity, the temperature being 25°C in both cases. The moisture content values of the samples when in equilibrium at the two humidities are given, as are also the movements corresponding to the particular moisture content range.

It is necessary to stress here that shrinkage and movement are not directly related one to the other. For example, it is possible that a wood may shrink quite appreciably in drying from the green to 12 per cent moisture content, yet it may undergo comparatively small dimensional changes when subjected to a given range of atmospheric conditions in service. The reason is that the so-called 'fibre saturation point', or the moisture content value at which appreciable shrinkage begins to take place, varies considerably with the different species. Furthermore, the moisture content change of one timber corresponding to any given range of atmospheric conditions often differs considerably from that of another (*vide* western red cedar and Scots pine).

Shrinkage values, therefore, are useful only in estimating roughly the dimensional allowances necessary in converting green material. It must be pointed out, however, that a further allowance for possible losses owing to distortion must be added.

Movement values, on the other hand, give some indication of how the dried timber will tend to behave when subjected to atmospheric changes in service. A so-called 'stable' timber is one that exhibits comparatively small dimensional changes in passing from the 90 to the 60 per cent humidity conditions.

Finally, it may be remarked that the moisture content values in the 60 per cent humidity conditions correspond roughly to the average values likely to be attained by wood exposed to normal indoor conditions in this country. For most timbers, this average will be of the order of 12–13 per cent moisture content, but for some, e.g. western red cedar, it will be more nearly 9–10 per cent moisture content.

Wood bending properties

In assessing the bending properties of a timber, the most important factor is the minimum radius of curvature at which a reasonable percentage of faultless bends can be made for a given thickness of clear material. This radius varies according to whether the timber is bent with or without a supporting strap after a suitable softening treatment, or is bent cold in the form of thin laminate at a moisture content of about 12 per cent. The ratio R/S, where R is the radius and S is the thickness of the wood, at which breakages during bending do not exceed 5 per cent, is determined by test.

Other assessments are obtained from observations of the end pressures, bending moments and general behaviour of selected pieces bent to a standard radius of curvature.

Classification of timbers according to their steam-bending properties is, however, based mainly on the minimum bending radius of sound, clear specimens 2·54 cm (1 in.) thick at a moisture content of about 25 per cent. The specimens are subjected to saturated steam at atmospheric pressure for a period of not less than 45 minutes before bending. The following classification of the steam-bending properties of woods has been adopted by the Laboratory. For purposes of comparison, it may be noted that with a very good bending species such as home-grown beech (*Fagus sylvatica*), specimens 2·54 cm (1 in.) thick may safely be bent to a radius as small as 3·81 cm (1·5 in.), or a specimen 5·08 cm (2 in.) thick to a radius of about 7·62 cm (3 in.).

Radius of curvature at which breakages during bending should not exceed 5 per cent	Classification of bending properties (material supported and 2·54 cm (1 in.) thick)
Less than 15·2 cm (6 in.)	Very good
15·2–25·4 cm (6–10 in.)	Good
27·94–50·8 cm (11–20 in.)	Moderate
53·34–76·2 cm (21–30 in.)	Poor
Exceeding 53·34 cm (30 in.)	Very poor

It should be noted that with some species sufficient material was not available for comprehensive tests.

Bends of smaller radii than those given may be obtained and utilised if, for example, certain bending defects that may then occur can be removed in the final machining and finishing operations. On the other hand, it must be stressed that faultless bends of the radii listed for the various species can be produced only by using selected material and efficient bending methods.

Strength properties

The general term 'strength' as loosely applied to timber covers a number of specific strength properties, or mechanical properties as they are sometimes called, which the timber may possess to varying degrees. Thus, before the suitability, as regards 'strength', of a particular species can be assessed, consideration must be given to the specific mechanical properties appropriate to the proposed use.

Although, within very broad limits, most strength properties are proportional to the density of the species, there may be marked differences in certain specific properties between timbers of the same weight. Home-grown Douglas fir, having about the same weight, bending strength and toughness as Japanese larch, is 40 per cent stiffer and 25 per cent harder. For use as a beam, these two timbers are equally strong, but where shock resistance is important home-grown Douglas fir is definitely superior to Japanese larch. This example illustrates the importance, when comparing timbers, of taking into account the intended uses.

Generally, the strength requirements are covered by eight strength properties, which are discussed briefly below. Values for these properties are obtained from standard tests on samples of straight-grained timber free from all defects such as knots, checks, shakes or distorted grain, which are permitted in varying degree in timber of structural sizes and which influence the strength to a greater or lesser extent. These strength values of clear specimens are basic data and form the best foundation for the accurate comparison of one species with another. They are not tabulated in this handbook but can be found in Princes Risborough Laboratory Bulletins, Nos. 28 and 34, which are concerned principally with the strength properties of timbers.

(1) *Maximum bending strength* (*equivalent fibre stress at maximum load*)
This property is a measure of the maximum stress which can be developed in the timber when loaded slowly and continuously as a beam. It is of primary importance in timbers subjected to transverse bending.

(2) *Stiffness* (*modulus of elasticity*)
This property is of importance in determining the deflection of a beam under load—the greater the stiffness, the less the deflection. It is usually considered in conjunction with bending strength, as, for many uses, stiffness is an advantage. The modulus of elasticity is also the critical property determining the strength of a long column or strut, as distinct from a short column, for which maximum compressive strength (*q.v.*) is an essential property.

(3) *Energy consumed to total fracture* (*total work*)
This property is the measure of the ability of the timber to absorb energy and is, therefore, of particular importance where timbers are to be subjected to considerable bending under heavy loads as with scaffold planks, etc. This property is closely allied to the toughness of the timber.

(4) *Resistance to suddenly applied loads* (*impact*)
The standard method of determining this property is to drop a weight from increasing heights on to a beam supported near the ends. The height of drop at which the beam breaks is a measure of the property. A second method not specified in the British Standard is frequently used, namely, the toughness test. In this a test piece 25·4 cm (10 in.) long and 1·58 cm ($\frac{5}{8}$ in.) square, freely supported over a span of 20·32 cm (8 in.), is broken by a single blow centrally applied by a machine of the pendulum type. The energy absorbed by the test piece during fracture, calculated from the angles of swing of the pendulum before and after impact, is taken as a measure of the toughness of the timber.

Resistance to suddenly applied loads, as measured by these tests, is closely related to the afore-mentioned property, 'total work'. Species which rank high in the one often do so in the other. Where toughness in use is particularly desirable, high value for total work should be considered more important.

(5) *Maximum compressive strength, parallel to grain*
This property measures the ability of the timber to withstand loads applied on the end grain and is of importance where use as short columns or props is contemplated. Resistance to crushing parallel to the grain is required in many types of fastenings and should then be considered in conjunction with the two following properties.

3

(6) *Resistance to indentation (hardness)*

This property is measured by the resistance offered by the timber to indentation to a given depth by a standard steel ball. The property is of importance when timbers are jointed together, and also in timber to be used for such purposes as sports goods, bearing blocks, etc.

Although often referred to as hardness, this property does not include any measure of resistance to abrasion, a factor often underlying the everyday use of the word hardness. Special tests have been devised to measure the resistance of timbers to abrasion.

(7) *Shearing strength*

This property is a measure of the resistance of the timber when the forces acting on it tend to make one part slide over another, in a direction parallel to that of the grain. It is of considerable importance in beams, where the depth is large relative to the length, and, as mentioned above, in timbers fastened by bolts or other forms of connexion.

(8) *Resistance to cleavage (splitting)*

A high resistance to cleavage, taken in conjunction with the property of hardness, is of importance where timbers are to be nailed. On the other hand, a low value for this property may be an advantage where timbers have to be cleft before use. Resistance to splitting, with many species, may vary considerably with the plane of cleavage, the timber usually splitting more readily normal to the rings (radially) than parallel to the rings (tangentially).

Effect of moisture content on mechanical properties

Reduction of moisture content from that of the green state to a value generally between 25 and 30 per cent for most species has no effect on the mechanical properties of the timber, but further reduction causes a marked increase in most of the properties referred to above. Bending strength, stiffness, compressive strength, shearing strength and resistance to indentation are all increased as a result of seasoning, the degree of increase depending on the property, the species and the final moisture content. For many timbers, increases of over 100 per cent are shown in compressive strength on seasoning from the green state to a moisture content of 12 per cent.

Energy consumed to total fracture, resistance to suddenly applied loads and resistance to splitting are less affected by reduction of moisture content, some species showing slight decreases in these properties as a result of seasoning.

Defects caused by wood-boring insects

In certain circumstances timber may be attacked by various wood-boring insects, which differ in their choice of species and condition of wood—from standing trees to woodwork which has been in service for many years. Infestation in the tree or log usually dies out as the timber dries after felling and conversion but evidence of the attack remains permanently as wormholes and tunnels. Some timbers are more liable to attack than others but in all sapwood is much more susceptible than heartwood.

In softwoods, the most common types of insect damage are caused by the following:

Ambrosia (Pinhole borer) beetles (Platypodidae and Scolytidae)

Pinhole borer damage, caused by attack in standing trees, but more commonly in recently felled logs, is in general much less frequent in softwoods than in hardwoods. This defect, which may occur in heartwood as well as sapwood, takes the form of circular holes or short tunnels, of $0 \cdot 05$–$0 \cdot 32$ cm ($\frac{1}{50}$–$\frac{1}{8}$ in.) diameter, according to the insect responsible. Bore dust is absent but the walls of the tunnels and surrounding wood often show typical dark discoloration. The full extent of damage is not evident until infested logs are converted. Attack ceases when the timber is seasoned.

4

Longhorn beetles (Cerambycidae)

Attack by these insects, of which there are many species in tropical and temperate countries, results in the presence of dust-filled tunnels, oval in section and varying in size, in newly felled logs and sometimes in standing trees. Infestation is usually confined to bark and sapwood but occasionally tunnels enter the heartwood. Most of these insects attack green timber only and are relatively unimportant; of the few species which infest seasoned softwoods, the house longhorn beetle can cause serious damage.

Wood-wasps (Siricidae)

These insects, which occur in most temperate countries, attack dying or sickly coniferous trees and sound logs. Their larvae bore in the unseasoned sapwood and heartwood of most species, excavating tunnels circular in cross-section and filled with tightly packed bore dust. Although comparatively unimportant in most countries, attention has recently been drawn to this type of defect by the application of strict quarantine regulations in Australia to prevent the introduction of the insects in imported softwoods.

A similar type of defect, indistinguishable from wood-wasp damage, is caused by the beetle *Serropalpus barbatus* (Melandryidae).

Jewel beetles (Buprestidae)

Some softwoods (trees and logs) are attacked by these insects, which cease their activity after the timber is seasoned. The defect takes the form of larval tunnels, broadly oval and flattened in appearance and containing bore dust, in sapwood and occasionally in heartwood.

Powder-post beetles (Bostrychidae and Lyctidae)

The susceptibility of timber to attack by these insects is governed primarily by its starch content, which in softwoods is seldom adequate for infestation. With a few rare exceptions, softwoods are not attacked by the Lyctidae; the Bostrychidae, more abundant in the tropics, sometimes cause damage, when seasoned sapwood may be reduced to powder.

Furniture beetles (Anobiidae)

These insects are widespread in most temperate countries and are troublesome, particularly in old woodwork, including furniture, panelling and structural timbers. The seasoned sapwood of most softwoods is probably liable to attack by the common furniture beetle, the most frequent cause of woodworm damage in the United Kingdom; heartwood is not immune, especially if slight fungal decay is present. A comparatively unimportant type of damage may be caused by *Ernobius mollis* in structural timbers from which bark has not been completely removed; infestation is confined to the bark and outer sapwood.

Termites (White ants) (order Isoptera)

Information on the resistance of softwoods to attack by termites in tropical and sub-tropical countries is incomplete. The resistance of any particular timber may vary according to local conditions and the species of termite, e.g. of the subterranean type, nesting in the ground, or dry-wood species, infesting timber direct and not maintaining any contact with the ground. A list of British colonial timbers reputed from local record or experiment to be resistant to attack by these insects, and classified under countries, is given in Princes Risborough Laboratory Bulletin No. 24 entitled *The Protection of Buildings and Timber against Termites* (1951).

Under the heading 'Insect Attack' in the notes on individual timbers, brief comment is made of their susceptibility or resistance to attack by wood-boring insects. The absence of mention of any specific type of defect does not indicate that the timber is necessarily immune but that no information is available.

Resistance to marine borers

Timber used in sea or brackish waters is subject to attack by marine boring animals (*Teredo* spp., *Limnoria*, etc.). Marine borers are widely distributed but they are particularly destructive in tropical waters. Around the coast of Great Britain *Limnoria* appears to be generally active and although *Teredo* attack is spasmodic it is always liable to occur.

Most timbers have not sufficient resistance to marine borers to be of much use where they are liable to be attacked. Consequently no mention is made of this property in the descriptions of the timbers. The timbers listed below are generally recognised as being resistant but none of them is immune from attack. It will be seen that there is only one softwood, namely totara, among these timbers.

Afrormosia	Kapur
African padauk	Manbarklak*
Andaman padauk	Muninga
Basralocus*	Okan*
Billian*	Opepe*
Brush box*	Pyinkado*
Ekki*	Red louro*
Greenheart*	Southern blue gum
Iroko	Teak*
Ironbark	Totara* (softwood)
Jarrah	Turpentine*

Those marked with an asterisk are in general believed to be the best for marine work.

One of the most widely used materials for this purpose is pressure-creosoted timber, and long experience has shown that when the timber is thoroughly impregnated it will last a very long time.

Natural durability

In this country the term durability generally refers to the resistance of a timber to fungal decay and it is used in this sense here. Durability is of importance only where a timber is liable to become damp, as, for example, where it is used out of doors. It is of no consequence where a timber is used for purposes such as furniture where it can always be kept dry because, under these conditions, wood-destroying fungi are not active.

The durability of most timbers varies a great deal and even pieces cut from the same tree will often show wide differences, so it is only possible to speak of durability in approximate terms. In this handbook it is described by means of five grades as follows:

Grade of durability	Approximate life in contact with the ground (years)
Very durable	More than 25
Durable	15–25
Moderately durable	10–15
Non-durable	5–10
Perishable	Less than 5

All available information has been used in classifying the timbers, including laboratory tests and field tests made both in this country and abroad and also records of performance in actual use. The classification is primarily a relative one but, from the results of field tests being carried out at the Princes Risborough Laboratory, it has been possible to give in the table some quantitative meaning to each grade. Thus timbers of the very durable class may be expected to have an average life of over 25 years when used in contact with the ground in this country. The life stated for each grade relates to material of $5·08 \times 5·08$ cm (2×2 in.) section. Larger sizes will, of course, last longer, but the increase will depend on the kind of wood. In general, in larger sizes the durable woods will last much longer, but perishable ones only slightly longer, than the figures given. Timber used externally, but not in contact with the ground, will generally have a much longer life than that indicated by its grading.

Except where otherwise stated, the durability given refers to heartwood; the sapwood of almost all timbers is either perishable or non-durable. It is essential to remember this when dealing with timbers which may sometimes contain a high proportion of sapwood, and therefore will then be less durable than their grading suggests.

When choosing a timber for a structure which is to be exposed to conditions conducive to decay, it is of the utmost importance to decide, before the timber is acquired, how the required durability is going to be obtained. Usually there is a choice between using a naturally durable wood and a less durable one treated with a preservative. If a less durable wood is chosen it is desirable to select one which can be easily treated. This is particularly important where a very long life is required. Where a timber has to be selected for other properties, or where the choice is limited by price or availability, the question of durability is often neglected: there is then a risk that the timber chosen may not be durable enough in its natural state or permeable enough to allow of adequate preservative treatment.

Amenability to preservative treatment

The ease with which a timber can be impregnated with preservatives is important when it is to be used under conditions favourable to decay or to attack by insects or marine borers, as, for example, for poles, sleepers, or piling. Only a few timbers are durable enough in their natural state to give long service when used for such purposes and it is now common practice to employ preserved timber, which is not only cheaper but, if the preservative treatment is properly done, will usually outlast a durable wood.

It is not possible to preserve all timbers equally well. Some are virtually impenetrable and cannot be given a satisfactory treatment, whereas others are permeable and can be heavily impregnated with preservatives. Where a long life is required under exposed conditions it is essential, therefore, to choose a timber which can be well impregnated. In this connexion it is important to remember that the sapwood of a timber, although nearly always perishable, is usually much more permeable than the heartwood. Consequently, round timbers containing an outer band of sapwood can generally be impregnated much more satisfactorily, and can be made to last longer, than sawn material of the same species.

The terms used in this handbook to describe the extent to which a timber can be impregnated with preservatives are defined as follows:

Permeable
These timbers can be penetrated completely under pressure without difficulty, and can usually be heavily impregnated by the open tank process.

Moderately resistant
These timbers are fairly easy to treat, and it is usually possible to obtain a lateral penetration of the order of 0·63–1·9 cm ($\frac{1}{4}$–$\frac{3}{4}$ in.) in about 2–3 hours under pressure.

Resistant
These timbers are difficult to impregnate under pressure and require a long period of treatment. It is often very difficult to penetrate them laterally more than about 0·32–0·63 cm ($\frac{1}{8}$–$\frac{1}{4}$ in.). Incising is often used to obtain a better treatment.

Extremely resistant
These timbers absorb only a small amount of preservative even under long pressure treatments. They cannot be penetrated to an appreciable depth laterally and only to a very small extent longitudinally.

Working properties

The notes on the working properties of the timbers described in this handbook are based generally on the behaviour of normal kiln-dried material (moisture content from 10 to 14 per cent). It should be realised that, particularly with the denser timbers, drier material will have a greater resistance to cutting and an increased dulling effect on tools. The increased brittleness at the lower moisture content is, however, of assistance in planing timber having wavy or disturbed grain, as the chips break more easily and such tearing as occurs is less severe.

References to standard working conditions relate to operations carried out on ordinary commercial machines with cutter positions, speeds, etc., as provided by the manufacturer. The cutting angle of about 32° found on most planing machines is suitable for most softwoods but a reduction in the angle improves the finish of dense, wavy-grained timbers such as yew. It is seldom possible to change the angle at which a cutter is mounted in a machine and alteration of the cutting angle has to be made by honing or grinding a bevel on the leading face of the cutter. With a large number of softwoods, it is essential to maintain the tools in a sharp condition in order to cut the springwood cleanly and to minimise the defect known as 'raised grain' on planed and moulded surfaces. The use of square cutterblocks and an efficient waste-removal system give improved results with those timbers that tend to chip-bruise in planing.

The remarks on nailing and screwing refer to the behaviour of the timber when normal care is taken to use nails of suitable size and to pre-bore correctly for screws. The notes on gluing similarly assume good conditions for application and setting.

Recommendations are made concerning the best types of saw for working the various timbers. Full particulars of the several types are given in Appendix I. The teeth of saws cutting resinous timbers have less tendency to collect gum as their pitch is increased. Although such timbers can generally be cut satisfactorily with the saws indicated in the Appendix, it is often advantageous, where severe choking and gumming up of saw teeth is experienced, to employ type A saws having a suitable amount of hook.

Veneer and plywood

Although more than half the world's annual plywood production is made from 'Douglas fir', fewer individual species of softwood than of hardwood are employed. Information on the softwoods for this purpose is sparse and often conflicting, and notes have been given only for those upon which there is general agreement.

Uses

Typical uses for each timber are mentioned, with special reference to the wood-using industries of the United Kingdom. The list of uses is in no way exhaustive; it is intended rather to indicate the kind of work for which each timber is suited.

8

The timbers

Alerce

Fitzroya cupressoides

The tree Alerce grows to a height of 30·5 m, but on most favourable sites it reaches 39·6–45·7 m. The diameter averages about 1·2 m but in some regions is as much as 2·7 m. The tree is found in the central part of Chile between the 39° and 43°S latitudes. It is a typical species of low swamp forest.

The timber —general description A brownish-red softwood with rather unusual features which raise it out of the ordinary softwood class. The great age and exceptionally slow growth of the trees account for the high quality of much of the timber produced. Thus it is typically straight-grained, comparatively free from knots and other natural defects, with a narrow sapwood and of a very fine, even texture. The weight of the seasoned timber is reported to vary from as little as 290 kg/m³ (18 lb/cu. ft) to about 640 kg/m³ (40 lb/cu. ft); the average is probably about 420 kg/m³ (26 lb/cu. ft).

Mechanical properties In its major mechanical properties, alerce closely resembles obeche, but its weight, hardness and shear strength are higher and are of the same order as those of Baltic redwood.

Natural durability Durable.

Preservative treatment Moderately resistant.

Working properties The timber works easily in all hand and machine operations and has very little blunting effect on the tools. In general it machines to a good finish but the cutting edges should be kept well sharpened, especially in working on end grain, as there is a tendency to crumble or break away under the tool. The working properties are comparable with those of sequoia. It takes glue, stain and polish satisfactorily. Saw type E is recommended.

Tests to determine the degree of suitability of alerce as pencil slats showed that it was not quite so uniform in resistance to cutting as 'Virginian pencil cedar', but with a suitable softening treatment it would probably be satisfactory.

Uses The timber has been imported into the United Kingdom, but is not regularly supplied. In Chile it is used for vats, honey barrels, furniture, joinery, etc. The small trees are used in the round for masts and spars.

Cedar

Cedrus spp.

Atlantic (Atlas) cedar (*Cedrus atlantica*), cedar of Lebanon (*Cedrus libani*) and deodar (*Cedrus deodara*) are the true cedars. These should not be confused with other cedars of commerce, whether softwood or hardwood, so called because of the natural fragrance of their wood which may resemble that of *Cedrus*.

The tree Deodar is a native of the Western Himalayas and grows to a height of 61 m with a 2·1 m diameter. Atlantic cedar is found in Algeria and Morocco while the Lebanon cedar is native to the Middle East. The last two do not grow as large as the deodar cedar and are from 36·6 to 45·7 m high and 1·2–1·5 m in diameter. In Great Britain they are grown mainly as ornamental trees.

9

The timber **—general description**	The heartwood, which is strongly scented and somewhat resinous, is of a light brown colour, usually distinct from the paler sapwood. Annual rings are clearly marked by the contrast between springwood and the dense summerwood zones. The average weight of seasoned timber of moderate growth is about 560 kg/m³ (35 lb/cu. ft).
Mechanical properties	No strength data are available for any of these cedars grown in this country. They are, however, said to produce rather soft, brittle timber. Figures for deodar grown in the Himalayan district show that the timber is slightly heavier than that of Baltic redwood but similar in bending strength and stiffness. Its hardness is appreciably greater but it lacks shock resistance and toughness.
Resistance to insect attack	Deodar is occasionally attacked by ambrosia (pinhole borer) beetles and by longhorn beetles, but is recorded in tests in India as resistant to termites. Little is known of attack in the other cedars but there are records of damage by *Sirex* in cedar of Lebanon and by longhorn beetles in Atlantic cedar.
Natural durability	Durable.
Preservative treatment	Resistant. The sapwood appears to vary from permeable to resistant.
Working properties	The only information available is on cedars grown in Great Britain. These work easily by hand and machine tools and have little dulling effect on cutting edges. Large knots and inbark sometimes cause trouble in machining and care is usually needed to prevent breaking away at the tool exit when the cut is across the grain. Otherwise a good finish can be obtained in most operations, provided that cutting edges are kept sharp. The timbers have good nailing properties and take stain, varnish and paint well. Saw type C or D is recommended.
Uses	Deodar grown in India is used for sleepers, bridge building and house construction. Atlantic cedar is mainly used in Algeria and Morocco for sleepers, but is also employed in house building, furniture and for paving blocks. Cedar of Lebanon is a good interior decorative timber and is used locally for building. Cedars in Great Britain are usually park grown; their timber is usually very knotty but is suitable for garden furniture, gates, fencing and other outside work. Clear timber is suitable for doors and for interior joinery.

'Chile Pine'

Araucaria araucana

The tree	'Chile pine' occurs in a small area in the Coast Cordillera of the Chilean province of Arauco but is more abundant on both sides of the Andean divide at about 40°S latitude. The tree grows to 36·6 m in height, sometimes reaching 45·7 m, with a diameter of 1·2–1·5 m.
The timber **—general description**	This pale brown even-textured softwood compares closely with 'Parana pine' in weight (about 550 kg/m³ (34 lb/cu. ft) seasoned), grain and texture, but lacks the bright red streaks characteristic of the latter. Small brown flecks resembling pin knots are a common feature; these flecks also occur in 'Parana pine' but are generally not so noticeable in that species.
Seasoning	It appears to season fairly rapidly but the drying is a little inclined to patchiness. Numerous small knots tend to split somewhat but no checking is likely; distortion is in general slight. There is some evidence that denser timber, more prone to check, is sometimes encountered.

Kiln schedule J is recommended.

Shrinkage

Green to 12 per cent moisture content

Tangential	5 per cent
Radial	2·5 per cent

10

Movement

Moisture content in 90 per cent humidity	21 per cent
Moisture content in 60 per cent humidity	12·5 per cent
Corresponding tangential movement	2·6 per cent
Corresponding radial movement	1·4 per cent
Classification	medium movement

Working properties It offers a somewhat higher resistance to cutting than 'Parana pine' (*Araucaria angustifolia*) but, in other respects, it has similar working properties. It works fairly easily with hand and machine tools and has only a small blunting effect on their cutting edges. It cuts cleanly in most operations but has a tendency to crumble when worked on end grain. The absorption of stains is a little uneven. The timber takes nails well and varnishes and paints satisfactorily. Saw type D is recommended. The timber can be glued satisfactorily.

Uses It is used in South America for general building, carpentry and joinery.

Cypress

Cupressus spp.

The principal species grown in East Africa which have supplied timber for the United Kingdom market are *C. lindleyi* (*C. lusitanica*) and *C. macrocarpa*. The trees attain a height of 18·3–21·4 m with a bole of 0·6–0·9 m diameter, sometimes reaching 1·5 m. *C. macrocarpa* is a native of North America, where it has a very limited range along the coast of California. The tree has been extensively planted in Australia, New Zealand and in East and South Africa, in which countries it grows fast and on comparatively poor soils. It has also been planted to a limited extent in Great Britain. *C. lindleyi* (*C. lusitanica*) is a native of Mexico, extending through the mountains of Honduras and Guatemala. It grows to a height of about 30·5 m with a bole of 0·6 m diameter.

The heartwood is yellowish-brown to pinkish-brown and usually quite distinct from the paler sapwood, which is about 50–100 mm wide. The grain is usually straight and the texture fine and fairly even; the growth rings, marked by a narrow band of late-wood, are not conspicuous. Although for practical purposes the timber may be classed as non-resinous, resin cells are present and may appear as occasional brown streaks or flecks. The freshly seasoned timber has a cedar-like odour reminiscent of western red cedar but it becomes hardly noticeable after a time. The seasoned timber weighs about 450 kg/m³ (28 lb/cu. ft).

Woodworking tests on the East African timber have not been made, but home-grown *C. macrocarpa* of similar character worked readily with machine and hand tools and had little dulling effect on cutting edges, but its frequent knots were troublesome. Although straight-grained material finishes cleanly, surfaces with disturbed grain spoil by tearing. A little extra care is needed in working on end grain to prevent breaking away at the tool exit. The timber takes nails well and gives satisfactory results with the usual finishing treatments. Saw type D is recommended.

Cypress is a strong durable softwood used for constructional work, and especially suitable where the timber is in contact with the ground, or for external work generally.

'Douglas Fir'

Pseudotsuga menziesii (*P. taxifolia*)

Other names 'British Columbian pine', 'Columbian pine' (Great Britain); 'Oregon pine' (USA).

The tree 'Douglas fir' commonly attains a height of 45·7–61 m with a diameter of 0·9–1·8 m. Trees are, however, found up to more than 91·5 m high and of 4·6 m diameter. The bole is straight and frequently free of branches for 21·2 m. The northerly limit of the species is about 55°N, ranging down the western slopes of the Rockies, through Wyoming southwards to southern New Mexico and westwards to the Pacific coast.

It is most abundant in British Columbia, Washington, Oregon and on the western foothills of the Cascade Mountains.

The tree has been planted extensively in Great Britain and other parts of Europe and also in New Zealand and Australia.

The information refers to timber from both North America (Canada and the United States) and Great Britain unless otherwise stated.

The timber —general description

The heartwood when dry is of a light reddish-brown shade, which renders it clearly distinct from the pale-coloured sapwood. Supplies from North America show that material from the coastal region is lighter in colour and more uniform in texture than that of the mountainous region. The contrast between springwood and summerwood gives rise to a prominent growth ring figure, particularly marked on plain-sawn surfaces and rotary-cut veneers. The average weight of the seasoned timber is approximately 530 kg/m³ (33 lb/cu. ft). The wood is generally straight-grained but sometimes with a tendency to wavy or spiral grain. The North American timber is somewhat resinous but that grown in Great Britain is only moderately so. Timber coming from the old stands in North America is slow grown but the second-growth timber has about the same rate of growth as that produced from plantations in Great Britain.

Seasoning

The timber seasons rapidly and well without much checking or warping, but knots tend to split and loosen.

Kiln schedule K gives good results.

Shrinkage

Green to 12 per cent moisture content

Tangential	4 per cent
Radial	2·5 per cent

Movement (home-grown material)

Moisture content in 90 per cent humidity	19 per cent
Moisture content in 60 per cent humidity	12·5 per cent
Corresponding tangential movement	1·5 per cent
Corresponding radial movement	1·2 per cent
Classification	small movement

Mechanical properties

The timber obtained from North America and that grown in Great Britain have approximately the same strength properties. The timber obtained from the Pacific coastal districts is heavier, harder and stronger generally than that from the mountain area. 'Douglas fir' possesses, for its weight, good strength properties, especially in bending. Thus, when air-dry it is about 20 per cent heavier than Baltic redwood; but it is about 60 per cent stiffer, 40 per cent harder and more resistant to suddenly applied loads, and 30 per cent stronger in bending and in compression along the grain. Its resistance to splitting is about equal to that of Baltic redwood. Its strength properties are almost identical with those of commercial pitch pine.

Wood bending properties

No information based on tests carried out at the Laboratory is available, but it is considered unlikely that the species would prove suitable for solid bent work.

Resistance to insect attack

Logs are sometimes attacked by ambrosia (pinhole borer) beetles; damage by longhorn beetles is more frequent.

Damage by the jewel beetle, *Buprestis aurulenta*, in converted timber is occasionally recorded, and the timber is recorded in the West Indies as very susceptible to attack by drywood termites.

Natural durability

Moderately durable.

Preservative treatment

Resistant. The American mountain-grown 'Douglas fir' is reported to be much more difficult to impregnate than the coastal variety and probably belongs to the extremely resistant class.

Working properties

The timber works readily with hand and machine tools but with a little less ease and

12

slightly more dulling effect on cutting edges than the average quality of pine used for joinery purposes. Material grown in Great Britain tends to have hard and loose knots, which are troublesome in sawing and liable to damage cutting edges. Apart from a tendency for fast-grown material to splinter and break away at the tool exit where the cut is across the grain, a good finish is generally obtainable, provided that sharp tools are used. In planing and moulding, dulled cutters tend to drag and compress the soft springwood, which later expands and produces ridged surfaces. With a little care to avoid splitting in nailing, the timber takes nails and screws satisfactorily. It stains effectively and gives good results with the various finishing treatments when normal care is taken to prevent grain-raising. Material with high resin content should be kiln dried if intended to receive a varnished or painted finish for indoor purposes. Saw type D is recommended. The timber can be glued satisfactorily.

Veneer and plywood More veneer and plywood are produced from this species than from any other timber. The manufacture is confined to the Pacific coast of Canada and the United States.

Uses 'Douglas fir' is one of the few conifers from which clear timber or baulks of large dimension in long lengths can still be obtained. It is generally employed for heavy construction work, building (including laminated arches and roof trusses), interior and exterior joinery, poles, piles and paper pulp. It is widely used for the construction of vats and tanks for use in chemical plants, breweries and distilleries, for food-processing plants and textile manufacture, etc.

As a flooring timber it is suitable only for carrying comparatively light traffic and rift-sawn (edge-grain) material of sufficient density should be used, care being taken to avoid the inclusion of any plain-sawn timber.

Fir, Amabilis

Abies amabilis

Other names Red, lovely, alpine, silver, white, balsam, cascade fir; and 'larch'.

The tree Amabilis fir is found on the west coast of North America extending from Alaska southward to the northern part of California. It is known on the Queen Charlotte Islands, but is not common. It is mostly found on the western slopes, ranging from sea level at the northern extremities of its range to elevations of 915–1830 m south-wards. It grows to a height of 24·4–30·5 m, occasionally reaching 38 m, with a diameter of 0·45–0·9 m.

The timber —general description Amabilis fir is rather darker in colour than most species of true fir (*Abies*), but like these resembles spruce in general character although a little more open in texture and with darker summerwood bands. The seasoned timber weighs about 420 kg/m³ (26 lb/cu. ft).

Seasoning This timber can probably be seasoned with little degrade.

Kiln schedule L is recommended.

Mechanical properties Material of American origin is slightly lighter and appreciably softer than home-grown silver fir (*Abies alba*) but has otherwise very similar properties.

Resistance to insect attack Damage by ambrosia (pinhole borer) beetles sometimes present.

Natural durability Non-durable.

Working properties The timber works easily in all hand and machine operations and has little dulling effect on tools. In general it finishes cleanly, but sharp cutting edges are necessary, as otherwise there is some tendency to tearing. Knots loosened during seasoning are liable to fall from boards during sawing and machining. It takes nails well, stains effectively and gives good results with paint, varnish and polish. Saw type C or D is recommended.

13

Uses	The timber is used for building, interior finishing, general carpentry and box making. It is used on the Pacific coast for pulp.
Note	This timber and the rather similar grand fir, *A. grandis*, both loosely referred to as 'western balsam' (although this name is not strictly applicable to *A. amabilis*), are commonly shipped mixed with western hemlock.

Fir, Balsam

Abies balsamea

Other names	Fir, white and Canadian fir, 'silver pine', 'white spruce'.
The tree	Balsam fir extends from Newfoundland across Canada to the Lesser Slave Lake. The southern extremities are in Minnesota, Wisconsin and Michigan to Saginaw Bay and into the northern part of New York State. It grows along the Appalachian Mountains from western Massachusetts to south-west Virginia. The tree grows to a height of 15·3–21·4 m with a diameter of 0·3–0·6 m.
The timber —general description	The timber closely resembles spruce but is less lustrous and generally coarser in texture. A darker core surrounded by thick sapwood may be seen on the end of the log but in the converted timber practically no distinction between sapwood and heartwood is apparent. The seasoned timber weighs about 390 kg/m³ (24 lb/cu. ft).
Seasoning	This timber can probably be seasoned with little degrade. Kiln schedule L is recommended.
Mechanical properties	Balsam fir is lighter in weight and weaker in strength than Canadian spruce, particularly in resistance to shear.
Resistance to insect attack	Damage by ambrosia (pinhole borer) beetles, longhorn and Buprestid beetles is sometimes present. Damage by *Sirex* wood wasps has also been recorded.
Natural durability	Non-durable.
Preservative treatment	Resistant.
Working properties	The timber works easily in all hand and machine operations and has little dulling effect on tools. In general, it finishes cleanly but sharp cutting edges are necessary, as otherwise there is some tendency to tearing. Knots loosened during seasoning are liable to fall from boards during sawing and machining. It takes nails well, stains effectively and gives good results with paint, varnish and polish. Saw type C or D is recommended.
Uses	Balsam fir grows mixed with white and black spruce in eastern Canada and is logged without separating the species. The lumber is sold mixed, usually under the name of spruce. It is employed for building, interior joinery and general carpentry work. The material below sawmill size is used for pulp and pitprops.

Fir, Grand

Abies grandis

Other names	Lowland fir (Canada); western balsam fir, white fir (USA).
The tree	The range of this species is limited. In Canada it is found in the northern part of Vancouver Island and the southern coastal region and to a limited extent in the southern part of the interior wet belt. In the United States it extends along the coastal belt into California and in the mountain area of Washington and Idaho to the western slopes of the continental divide in northern Montana.

14

The tree has been planted to some extent in Great Britain, in western Scotland and England and in parts of Wales.

It grows to a height of 30·5–38 m with a diameter of 0·6–0·9 m. The bole is long, straight and clean.

The following description refers to timber grown in America unless otherwise stated.

**The timber
—general description**

The timber closely resembles that of Canadian spruce and European whitewood, though inclined to be somewhat coarser in texture and less lustrous. Owing to the larger size of the trees there is a higher proportion of clear timber. The wood is non-resinous, odourless and non-tainting when dry, typically straight-grained, nearly white to light brown in colour throughout, with no distinct heartwood. In the seasoned condition it weighs about 450 kg/m³ (28 lb/cu. ft).

Seasoning

Very little information based on laboratory tests is available. Such as there is tends to indicate that little or no difficulty is likely to be experienced in seasoning this timber.

Kiln schedule L is recommended.

Movement

Moisture content in 90 per cent humidity	18 per cent
Moisture content in 60 per cent humidity	12 per cent
Corresponding tangential movement	1·4 per cent
Corresponding radial movement	0·5 per cent
Classification	small movement

Mechanical properties

Grand fir is, on the whole, similar to silver fir (*Abies alba*) in its mechanical properties. When seasoned, its compressive strength along the grain and its stiffness are about the same as those of silver fir, its bending strength and resistance to splitting about 15 per cent less and its hardness and shear strength about 25 per cent less. Its shock resistance is high for its weight. Material grown in Great Britain is approximately 5 per cent lighter in weight and on a strength-weight basis is similar to the Canadian timber except in shock resistance, which is 30 per cent less, and toughness, which is about 20 per cent less.

Resistance to insect attack

Damage by ambrosia (pinhole borer) beetles, longhorn and Buprestid beetles is sometimes present.

Natural durability

Non-durable.

Preservative treatment

Resistant. The sapwood is permeable.

Working properties

The timber works easily in all hand and machine operations and has little dulling effect on tools. In general, it finishes cleanly but sharp cutting edges are necessary, as otherwise there is some tendency to tearing. Knots loosened during seasoning are liable to fall from boards during sawing and machining. It takes nails well, stains effectively and gives good results with paint, varnish and polish. Saw type C or D is recommended. The timber can be glued satisfactorily.

Uses

The timber is used for general carpentry, crates and boxes. In America it is used for pulp.

Fir, Noble

Abies procera (A. nobilis)

The tree

Noble fir attains a height of 45·7–61 m, sometimes reaching as much as 76·3 m, with a diameter of 1·8–2·4 m. The tree grows in northern Washington, its range extending south into California. It is most abundant in the Cascade Mountains of Washington. It has been planted to a limited extent in Great Britain.

**The timber
—general description**

A pale buff-coloured timber with darker summerwood bands; in general appearance it is not unlike western hemlock but is usually coarser in texture and slightly lighter in weight. The seasoned timber weighs about 420 kg/m³ (26 lb/cu. ft).

15

The timber of this species is generally of fast growth in this country and consequently much coarser in texture than the American product.

Seasoning   This timber can probably be seasoned with little degrade.

Kiln schedule L is recommended.

Mechanical properties   The weight and strength properties of noble fir are of the same order as those of silver fir (*Abies alba*).

Natural durability   Non-durable.

Preservative treatment   Resistant.

Working properties   The trees of this species yield a high proportion of straight-grained, clear material. In comparison with grand fir, the timber is usually more uniform but otherwise it has similar working properties. The timber can be glued satisfactorily.

Veneer and plywood   Logs are used in the western United States for the manufacture of plywood.

Uses   It is sometimes exported under its own name, though some may be included in consignments of hemlock or spruce. Locally, it is used for interior finishing of buildings and in the box and packing-case trade.

Fir, Silver or Whitewood[1]

Abies alba (A. pectinata)

Other name   'European silver pine' (Great Britain).

The tree   Silver fir attains, under favourable conditions, a height of 45·7 m and a diameter of 1·8 m but is more often found to be about 38 m with a 0·9–1·2 m diameter. Its northern limits in its natural conditions are through mid-Europe, and southerly it is found in northern Spain, Corsica and the Balkans. The eastern extremities are from Posen, south through Warsaw to the Carpathians. Except where otherwise stated the following information refers primarily to the timber grown in Great Britain. It may be taken to apply generally to the imported timber provided that allowance is made for differences due to growth and grading.

The timber —general description   The timber closely resembles European spruce, but is slightly less lustrous. The seasoned timber weighs about 480 kg/m³ (30 lb/cu. ft); the green weight (116 per cent moisture content) is about 800 kg/m³ (50 lb/cu. ft).

Seasoning   This timber seasons very rapidly with little tendency to warp, but some tendency to check and split and for knots to loosen and split.

Kiln schedule K is recommended.

Shrinkage

Green to 12 per cent moisture content

Tangential	5 per cent
Radial	2 per cent

Mechanical properties   The seasoned timber is about 20 per cent harder than Baltic redwood, but in other strength properties the two timbers are very similar. It is about 40 per cent harder on the side grain than imported spruce but not very different in other strength properties.

Resistance to insect attack   Damage by ambrosia (pinhole borer) beetles, longhorn and Buprestid beetles is sometimes present. It is also subject to damage by *Sirex*.

---

[1] Small quantities of home-grown timber may be offered under the name of silver fir but the chief importance of this species is that it is included with European spruce in shipments of whitewood from Central and Southern Europe.

16

Natural durability	Non-durable.
Preservative treatment	Moderately resistant. The sapwood is permeable.
Working properties	The working properties of the timber are somewhat similar to those of European spruce, though its knots are less troublesome. It works easily in all hand and machine operations but, owing to its softness, needs sharp, thin-edged tools to obtain a good, smooth finish. It takes nails well and responds satisfactorily to the usual finishing treatments. Saw type C or D is recommended.
Veneer and plywood	Logs are often used in northern Europe in conjunction with *Pinus sylvestris* for the manufacture of plywood.
Uses	Sawn into lumber, it is used for the same purposes as European spruce.

Hemlock, Eastern
Tsuga canadensis

Other name	White hemlock (Canada).
The tree	Eastern hemlock reaches a height of 18·3–22·9 m and a dimaeter of 0·6–1·2 m. It is found in North America, ranging from Nova Scotia, southern Quebec and Ontario to eastern Minnesota, and south to northern Georgia and Alabama. Its optimum size is reached in North Carolina and Tennessee.
The timber —general description	The timber of this species is inferior to that of the better-known western hemlock, being relatively coarse-textured and cross-grained. The wood is pale brown in colour, less lustrous than western hemlock but with a more prominent growth ring figure resembling that of 'Douglas fir'. The average weight is about 470 kg/m³ (29 lb/cu. ft), seasoned.
Seasoning	This timber is reputed to be rather difficult to season on account of its tendency to twist. Careful piling is recommended.
	Kiln schedule K is recommended.

Shrinkage

Green to 12 per cent moisture content

Tangential	4·5 per cent
Radial	2 per cent

Mechanical properties	Unseasoned eastern hemlock does not differ markedly in mechanical properties from western hemlock, but the air-dry timber is 20–30 per cent inferior in bending strength, stiffness and resistance to impact loads. It is 30 per cent stronger in shear, but other differences in strength are negligible from the practical point of view.
Resistance to insect attack	Logs are sometimes attacked by ambrosia (pinhole borer) beetles.
	Seasoned timber is recorded in Australia as susceptible to attack by the common furniture beetle.
Natural durability	Non-durable.
Preservative treatment	Resistant.
Working properties	The working properties of the timber are similar to those of western hemlock but it is reported to be inferior in nail holding.
Uses	Owing to its coarse grain the timber is employed only for inferior work such as paling boards, outsheds, etc. Its bark is a source of tannin extract.

17

Hemlock, Western

Tsuga heterophylla

The tree Western hemlock reaches a height of 61 m with a diameter of 1·8–2·4 m. It ranges from southern Alaska southwards to California, extending east over the mountains of British Columbia, northern Washington and Idaho to the western slopes of the continental divide and the western slopes of the Cascade Mountains. This species has been planted to some extent in Great Britain, where it grows well and makes a good forest crop. The information below refers to timber grown in Canada and the United States, except where stated otherwise.

The timber —general description A non-resinous softwood timber, without odour (when dry), and non-tainting. It is typically straight-grained and of fairly even texture. The wood is pale brown in colour and somewhat lustrous. The darker summerwood bands, which usually have a reddish or slightly purplish cast, produce a well marked growth-ring figure, but this is less prominent than that of 'Douglas fir'. The average weight is about 490 kg/m³ (30 lb/cu. ft), seasoned.

Seasoning It is stated that this timber, when green, has a very high moisture content and does not season as rapidly or as easily as British Columbian 'Douglas fir'. With care it can be kiln dried very satisfactorily. The tendency towards fine surface checking needs to be guarded against, but distortion should not give much trouble. Some difficulty may be experienced in extracting the moisture from the centre of thick planks.

With home-grown material kiln schedule L gave good results. The timber seasoned very rapidly with virtually no checking but cup and twist were moderately bad in some instances.

Shrinkage

Green to 12 per cent moisture content

Tangential	4 per cent
Radial	2·8 per cent

Movement

Moisture content in 90 per cent humidity	21 per cent
Moisture content in 60 per cent humidity	13 per cent
Corresponding tangential movement	1·9 per cent
Corresponding radial movement	0·9 per cent
Classification	small movement

Mechanical properties Compared with Canadian 'Douglas fir', western hemlock is when seasoned about 10 per cent lighter in weight, with correspondingly lower values of bending and compressive strength, hardness and resistance to shear; it is 30 per cent less stiff and possesses only half the toughness but has equal resistance to cleavage. Its weight and strength properties closely resemble those of Baltic redwood.

Resistance to insect attack Logs are susceptible to attack by ambrosia (pinhole borer) beetles. Damage by Siricid wood-wasps is occasionally present.

The sapwood of seasoned timber is liable to attack by the common furniture beetle. Dark brown or black resinous scars ('black check') are sometimes present in sapwood and heartwood and are caused by fly larvae (Syrphidae) boring in the cambium of living trees.

Natural durability Non-durable.

Preservative treatment Resistant.

Working properties The timber works readily in all hand and machine operations and has little dulling effect on cutting edges. It is about 20 per cent less easy to work than imported redwood of equivalent grade, and its knots are harder and more brittle. The relative softness of the springwood requires the use of sharp tools for clean cutting, and in end-grain working, e.g. scribing, mortising, etc., the material must be properly supported at the tool exit to obviate chipping out. There is a tendency to chip-bruising in planing and,

18

for the best finish, the waste removal system must be efficient and the cutters should be honed free from wire-edge. The timber has fairly good nailing and screwing properties but it is advisable to bore for nails used near the ends of seasoned boards. It stains effectively and gives good results with polish, varnish and paint. Saw type C is recommended. The timber can be glued satisfactorily.

Veneer and plywood Logs are used in the western United States and Canada for the manufacture of plywood.

Uses The timber from Canada and the United States is extensively exported to all parts of the world. It is used for constructional purposes, joinery, etc., and can be obtained in large baulk sizes.

Consignments of western hemlock frequently contain a percentage of fir (*Abies* spp.).

Note From limited tests on thinnings from young plantations of western hemlock grown in Great Britain it appears that the timber is very similar to the imported, except that as the trees are comparatively young the material has considerably more knots and is faster grown.

'Incense Cedar'
Calocedrus decurrens (*Libocedrus decurrens*)

The tree 'Incense cedar' usually grows to a height of 24·4–30·5 m and sometimes as much as 45·7 m with a tall, straight, irregularly lobed bole of 0·9–1·2 m diameter and occasionally as much as 1·8 m. It is found most abundantly on the Sierra Nevada of central California but ranges from Oregon to southern California in the mountainous districts.

The timber
—general description 'Incense cedar' resembles the better-known 'western red cedar' in general character. Both are soft, light-weight, durable woods of medium texture showing variation in colour from dark chocolate-brown to a salmon colour, and both have a spicy, cedar-like odour. They soon tone down to a more uniform brown colour, the 'incense cedar' usually becoming light brown, whereas 'western red cedar' attains a darker russet or reddish-brown; the lack of lustre and the less prominent summerwood zones also help to distinguish incense cedar. The seasoned timber weighs about 400 kg/m³ (25 lb/cu. ft). The tree is rather prone to rot in the heart, known as peckiness, sometimes causing severe loss in conversion.

Mechanical properties In its mechanical properties this timber closely resembles 'western red cedar' but is slightly heavier.

Resistance to insect attack Damage by longhorn and Buprestid beetles is sometimes present.

Working properties The timber works easily and has very little dulling effect on tool edges. It cuts cleanly in most operations provided that sharp cutters are employed. The timber takes paint well and gives good results with stains and polishes. Saw type C or D is recommended.

Uses The timber is not often exported. It is very durable and is used in the United States for fencing, laths and shingles, interior finishing of buildings, in the furniture industry and for pencils. Locally it is used extensively in the construction of flumes.

Kauri, East Indian
Agathis dammara (*A. alba*)

The commercial timber is commonly known as Borneo kauri, Sarawak kauri, etc., according to the country of origin, also as bindang or bendang in Sarawak and as menghilan in Sabah. The tree varies in size considerably with topographical conditions, reaching a diameter of only 0·76–0·9 m on the lowlands of Sarawak, while in the

Sabah hills it attains a 1·5–1·8 m diameter with a height of 61 m. The bole is straight and cylindrical but is apt to retain its branches, making the timber knotty.

It has a fairly wide distribution, from Indo-China through Malaysia, Sarawak and Sabah to New Guinea.

The timber is pale pinkish-brown in colour and of fine, even texture, straight-grained, lustrous and with barely distinguishable growth rings. It more closely resembles Queensland kauri than the heavier and darker-coloured New Zealand kauri. The seasoned timber weighs about 480 kg/m³ (30 lb/cu. ft).

It is a softwood which turns well and can be used for furniture and interior joinery. The wood is moderately durable and damage by ambrosia (pinhole borer) beetles is sometimes present.

The tree is tapped for Manila copal which is used in the varnish industry.

Kauri, New Zealand

Agathis australis

Other name 'Kauri pine' (Great Britain).

The tree Kauri grows to an average height of about 30·5 m, with an average diameter of 1 m, though there are trees of very large diameter.

Its distribution is from north of latitude 38°S to the extreme north of the North Island of New Zealand, at altitudes from sea level to 763 m.

The timber —general description A valuable softwood timber, straight-grained, with a fine, even, silky texture and a lustrous surface. The colour is normally a pale greyish-brown; in trees with heavy infiltrations of resin it may be dark reddish- or yellowish-brown. The resin does not occur in ducts, as in the true pines, and is not fluid in seasoned timber, so that the painting properties of the wood are not affected. Irregularities of the grain sometimes produce an attractive mottling on flat-sawn surfaces. Seasoned timber weighs about 580 kg/m³ (36 lb/cu. ft).

Seasoning It is stated that if the timber is of good quality it seasons well, but not rapidly, without much checking, warping or shrinkage. Apparently, however, timber of poorer growth is liable to warp. It is reported to have appreciable longitudinal shrinkage.

Kiln schedule J would appear to be suitable for this timber.

Movement

Moisture content in 90 per cent humidity	19 per cent
Moisture content in 60 per cent humidity	13 per cent
Corresponding tangential movement	1·6 per cent
Corresponding radial movement	1 per cent
Classification	small movement

Mechanical properties New Zealand kauri, in both the green and the air-dry state, is practically equal to commercial pitch pine in all its strength properties, except that in the unseasoned condition it splits about 30 per cent more readily and in the air-dry condition is about 25 per cent weaker in compression along the grain.

Resistance to insect attack Damage by ambrosia (pinhole borer) beetles and longhorn beetles is sometimes present. The wood is also subject to attack by termites, weevils and the common furniture beetle.

Natural durability Moderately durable.

Preservative treatment Probably resistant.

Working properties The timber works easily by hand and machine tools and with a very slight dulling effect on their cutting edges. It planes and moulds to a clean, smooth finish and gives good results in most other operations. In boring, mortising, etc., it needs to be properly supported at the exit of the tool, particularly with flat-sawn material, as it is inclined to break away easily. Figured material has a slight tendency to pick up in planing; this can, however, generally be remedied by using a cutting angle of about 20°. The timber has good nailing and screwing properties, takes stain uniformly and effectively, paints well and polishes excellently. Saw type D is recommended. The timber can be glued satisfactorily.

Veneer and plywood	It is reported to be used for the manufacture of plywood for packaging.
Uses	The limited amount of New Zealand kauri available restricts its use to special purposes and most of the timber is used in New Zealand. The high and medium quality material is employed for vats, wooden machinery and boat building and the lower grades have been used to some extent in building construction.

Kauri, Queensland

Agathis robusta, A. palmerstonii and *A. microstachya*

Other names	'Queensland kauri pine' (Great Britain); South Queensland kauri: *A. robusta* (Australia); North Queensland kauri: *A. palmerstonii* and *A. microstachya* (Australia).
The tree	Queensland kauri grows to a maximum height of 45·7 m, with diameters up to 2·4 or 3 m and averaging about 1·4 m.
	South Queensland kauri has a very limited range, within about 60 miles of Maryborough, and is almost extinct. North Queensland kauri (mainly *A. palmerstonii*) is found along the north-east coast of Queensland, between Cooktown and Townsville, and is limited in quantity. Pure plantations have been established though not extensively.
The timber —general description	Like the more valuable New Zealand kauri, the Australian timber is straight-grained with a fine uniform texture. The colour varies from pale cream to a light brown or medium pinkish-brown. It is appreciably lighter in weight than the New Zealand timber, weighing about 480 kg/m³ (30 lb/cu. ft), seasoned.
Seasoning	It is stated that the timber can be seasoned fairly quickly without degrade. There is slight collapse in drying but insufficient to justify reconditioning.
	Kiln schedule J is recommended.

Shrinkage

Shrinkage from green to 12 per cent moisture content is stated to be

Tangential	3·5 per cent
Radial	2·2 per cent

Mechanical properties	Data from Australia on *A. palmerstonii* indicate that, although similar in many of its properties to the New Zealand species, it is appreciably lighter in weight and deficient in bending strength and stiffness.
Wood bending properties	It is reputed to possess moderately good bending properties but no exact data are available.
Resistance to insect attack	It is subject to attack by the common furniture beetle.
Natural durability	Non-durable.
Veneer and plywood	It is reported to be used for the manufacture of plywood for packaging.
Uses	Queensland kauri is used for high-class joinery and cabinet work and is particularly suitable for battery separators, pattern making and for butter boxes. It has also been employed for butter churns. The limited amount available restricts its use, even in Australia.

21

Larch, European

Larix decidua (L. europaea)

The tree European larch attains a height of 30·5–45·7 m and a diameter of 0·9–1·2 m. The stem, if grown in forests, is long, cylindrical and clean for two-thirds of its length. The tree has a natural distribution in the Alps, the Silesia-Moravia boundary, western Poland and into Russia and the Carpathians. It has been planted extensively throughout other parts of Europe and Great Britain and to a limited extent in the north-eastern United States. Information given refers to timber grown in Great Britain, but may be taken generally to refer to that grown throughout Europe.

The timber —general description Larch is a very valuable home-grown softwood; when well grown it is straight-grained and relatively free from knots; the resinous heartwood is pale reddish-brown to brick-red in colour, sharply differentiated from the narrow light-coloured sapwood. Annual rings are clearly marked by the contrasting light springwood and dark summerwood zones. Larch is one of the heavier softwood timbers, averaging about 590 kg/m³ (37 lb/cu. ft), seasoned, and about 720 kg/m³ (45 lb/cu. ft), green (50 per cent moisture content).

Seasoning This timber seasons fairly rapidly with some tendency to distort and for knots to split and to loosen.

Kiln schedule H has proved satisfactory.

Shrinkage
Green to 12 per cent moisture content

Tangential	4·5 per cent
Radial	3 per cent

Movement

Moisture content in 90 per cent humidity	19 per cent
Moisture content in 60 per cent humidity	13 per cent
Corresponding tangential movement	1·7 per cent
Corresponding radial movement	0·8 per cent
Classification	small movement

Mechanical properties Disregarding yew, for which full strength data are not available, larch is the hardest and toughest of the home-grown softwoods. The air-dry timber is about 50 per cent harder than Baltic redwood and slightly stronger in bending strength and toughness; its other mechanical properties differ very little from those of redwood.

Resistance to insect attack Damage by ambrosia (pinhole borer) beetles, longhorn beetles and *Sirex* is sometimes present. Larch is also attacked by the common furniture beetle.

Natural durability Moderately durable.

Preservative treatment Resistant. The sapwood is moderately resistant.

Working properties The timber saws and machines fairly readily and finishes cleanly in most operations. There is generally a fair amount of wastage, however, in truing up seasoned, slash-sawn material and the knots, which are often hard and loose, tend to spoil the cutting edges of tools. It takes stain, paint and varnish satisfactorily but care is needed in nailing to avoid splitting. Saw type D is recommended.

Uses European larch is used for pitprops, stakes, transmission poles and piles. As sawn timber the heartwood is suitable for work where durability is of importance, such as boat planking, exterior work and in contact with the ground. It is harder and tougher than most conifers and is used where these properties are important factors.

Larch, Japanese

Larix kaempferi (L. leptolepis)

The tree The tree attains a height of 18·3–30·5 m with a diameter of 0·6–0·9 m. The bole is not as straight as that of European larch but it is cylindrical and clean for two-thirds of the way up when grown in forests. This larch is found in its natural state in the Shinano Province of Japan but natural forests are rare elsewhere. It has been planted extensively in Europe and Great Britain in the last half-century. The following information refers to timber from comparatively young trees grown in plantations in Great Britain.

The timber —general description Japanese larch closely resembles European larch in general appearance, having a reddish-brown heartwood sharply differentiated from the light-coloured sapwood, and clearly marked annual rings with well-defined summerwood bands. The timber from some sites in this country is of relatively fast growth and this is reflected in lower density figures than are usual for European larch, namely, about 530 kg/m³ (33 lb/cu. ft) for seasoned timber, and about 630 kg/m³ (39 lb/cu. ft), green (55 per cent moisture content). Elsewhere, however, the Japanese larch produces timber closely comparable with that of the European species.

Seasoning The timber seasons fairly rapidly with some tendency to warp, split and check.

Kiln schedule H is recommended.

Movement

Moisture content in 90 per cent humidity	18·5 per cent
Moisture content in 60 per cent humidity	12·5 per cent
Corresponding tangential movement	1·5 per cent
Corresponding radial movement	0·6 per cent
Classification	small movement

Mechanical properties Japanese larch does not differ very markedly from European larch in its mechanical properties. The seasoned timber is about 20 per cent less stiff and resistant to radial splitting and 30 per cent softer, but the differences in other mechanical properties are negligible.

Resistance to insect attack Damage by ambrosia (pinhole borer) beetles and *Sirex* is sometimes present.

Natural durability Moderately durable.

Preservative treatment Resistant. The sapwood is moderately resistant.

Working properties Home-grown timber works readily by hand and machine tools but the hard knots are troublesome. It is milder than European larch. Although the soft springwood zones are liable to tear or crumble, a clean finish is obtained in most operations if sharp cutting edges are used. The timber gives good results with varnish and paint but tends to split in nailing. Saw type D is recommended.

Uses The timber is very similar to that of European larch of comparable age and can be used for the same general purposes. As no large mature timber has been produced as yet in Great Britain it remains to be seen how the sawn timber compares with old growth European larch for exacting work such as boat building.

Larch, Tamarack

Larix laricina

Other names Tamarack, eastern larch (Canada and USA); eastern Canadian larch (Great Britain).

The tree The tree attains a height of 18·3–21·4 m and 0·3–0·6 m diameter. The trunk is cylindrical and straight with little taper. It is found from the Atlantic coast to Alaska, reaching into the Arctic Circle. It extends south to West Virginia and westward through north Indiana and Illinois and north-eastern Minnesota along the eastern foothills of the Rocky Mountains. It seldom forms pure stands but is abundant in Labrador and common along the margins of the barren lands. It is rare and local towards the southern limits of its range.

The timber —general description The timber has a rather coarse appearance owing to the presence of alternate bands of hard summerwood and softer springwood, and this effect is accentuated by relatively

23

wide growth rings, which are often irregular in width. The yellowish-brown heartwood is sharply differentiated from the narrow zone of sapwood. The average weight of the seasoned timber is about 560 kg/m³ (35 lb/cu. ft).

Seasoning This timber can probably be seasoned with little degrade.

Kiln schedule K is recommended.

Mechanical properties Tamarack is lighter, softer and generally weaker than western larch, and compares less favourably therefore with European larch, especially in shock resistance, in which it is inferior by some 40 per cent. In other mechanical properties it is 10–20 per cent inferior.

Resistance to insect attack Damage by ambrosia (pinhole borer) beetles is sometimes present.

Natural durability Moderately durable.

Preservative treatment Resistant.

Working properties The timber works fairly readily in most operations and has a slight blunting effect on tools. The working properties are comparable with those of European larch. There is a tendency to split in nailing and the more resinous material is reported to be somewhat unsatisfactory for staining or painting unless given special seasoning treatment. Saw type D is recommended.

Uses It is suitable for many of the same purposes as European larch.

Larch, Western
Larix occidentalis

The tree Western larch attains a height of 30·5–54·9 m and 0·9–1·2 m diameter with a very long, clean cylindrical bole. In Canada it is confined to the south-eastern part of British Columbia, spreading south into northern Oregon. Eastward it is found on the western slopes of the continental divide of northern Montana and westwards to the eastern slopes of the Cascade Mountains of Washington and northern Oregon. It is most abundant and reaches its largest size in northern Montana and northern Idaho.

The timber —general description This species of larch yields a timber rather similar in general appearance to a fine-textured type of British Columbia 'Douglas fir'. Like other larches it has a sharply defined heartwood and narrow sapwood. Its average weight is about 610 kg/m³ (38 lb/cu. ft), seasoned.

Seasoning It is stated that this timber seasons fairly well, though some difficulty is encountered with warping and checking.

Kiln schedule K is recommended.

Mechanical properties Western larch is one of the denser, harder softwoods having strength properties comparable with those of European larch. Seasoned, it is 25–30 per cent stronger in compression along the grain and stiffer in bending, but in hardness and other mechanical properties the two timbers are almost identical.

Resistance to insect attack Damage by longhorn and Buprestid beetles is sometimes present. The wood is susceptible to termite attack in the West Indies.

Natural durability Moderately durable.

Preservative treatment Resistant.

Working properties The timber works fairly readily in most operations and has a small blunting effect on tools. The working properties are comparable with those of European larch. There is

24

a tendency to split in nailing and the more resinous material is reported to be somewhat unsatisfactory for staining or painting unless given special seasoning treatment. Saw type D is recommended. The timber can be glued satisfactorily.

Veneer and plywood Logs are used in the western United States and Canada for the manufacture of plywood.

Uses The timber is used locally for a variety of commercial purposes such as railway sleepers, posts, mining timbers, general construction and exterior finishing of buildings.

Manio[1]

Podocarpus spp. and *Saxegothaea conspicua*

Other names Maniu, manilihuan, maniu hembra (*P. nubigenus*); maniu de la frontera (*P. salignus*); maniu macho (*Saxegothaea conspicua*).

The tree The two species of *Podocarpus* included in manio are rather different in form. *P. nubigenus* attains heights of from 9·2 to 24·4 m and diameters up to 0·6–0·9 m. The bole is of fairly good form. *P. salignus* grows to only 18·3 m high and 0·45 m in diameter and the trunk is often twisted. The trees are found singly, or in clumps on swampy land in the rain forests and alongside of streams. They occur in Chile in a narrow strip of territory bounded on the north by the River Maule and on the south by the island of Chiloe, i.e. between 35° and 43°S latitude.

Saxegothaea conspicua is a native of Chile, growing in swampy areas in the rain forests of Rio Mauleto, 45°S. The usual height is between 9·2 and 18·3 m and the number of exploitable trees per acre is too low in most localities to permit of extensive utilisation.

The timber —general description The wood is pale yellow to yellowish-brown or greyish-brown, the darker wood often with brown streaks; soft, straight-grained and of fine uniform texture. There are no conspicuous zones of dense latewood such as generally characterise the commercial softwoods of the northern hemisphere. Weight about 560 kg/m³ (35 lb/cu. ft), seasoned.

Seasoning No information based on tests is available but it is not expected that serious trouble would be experienced in the drying of this timber.

Kiln schedule J is recommended.

Mechanical properties The results of limited mechanical tests indicate that manio is similar in all strength properties to the East African species of *Podocarpus*. It is somewhat denser than Baltic redwood, some 25 per cent harder and slightly less resilient; thus it is less able to withstand shock-loading. In other strength properties it is comparable to Baltic redwood.

Resistance to insect attack There is occasional damage to logs by ambrosia (pinhole borer) beetles and by longhorn beetles.

Natural durability Probably durable.

Preservative treatment No information is available.

Working properties The timber works very easily by hand and machine tools and has similar working properties to those of various mild species of *Podocarpus* from Australasia and East Africa. It machines in general to a good, clean finish when cutting edges are kept sharp, but care is needed to prevent breaking away at the exit of the tool in operations where the timber is cut across the grain. There is a tendency to split in nailing, but good results are obtained with stain and polish. Saw type D is recommended.

[1] The timber called manio is made up principally of two species of *Podocarpus*, *P. nubigenus* and *P. salignus* (*P. chilinus*) and the allied *Saxegothaea conspicua*.

Uses	Occasionally imported into the United Kingdom and used mainly for joinery and carpentry work. In South America it is used for joinery, doors, windows and for honey barrels.

'Parana Pine'

Araucaria angustifolia (*A. brasiliana*)

The tree	The tree is found in Brazil on the plateau region of Rio Grande do Sul, Santa Catarina and Paraná and small areas of western São Paulo. It is also found in Paraguay and the northern Argentine. The tree reaches 24·4–36·6 m in height and up to 0·9–1·2 m in diameter. It has a clean straight bole for nearly its full length.
The timber —general description	The timber is brown at the heart, often with bright red streaks, but these may be entirely absent; this core is surrounded by pale-coloured sapwood. It is mostly straight-grained and more uniform in texture than softwoods of the northern hemisphere, the growth rings being more or less inconspicuous. It varies from light and soft to moderately hard and heavy, commonly 480 kg/m³ (30–40 lb/cu. ft), seasoned, average about 550 kg/m³ (34 lb/cu. ft). Green logs are too heavy to float.
Seasoning	It appears to be more difficult to season than most softwoods. The wood is variable in its seasoning properties, the darker-coloured material being very prone to split, distort and dry slowly. The load should be weighted to minimise distortion, and a prolonged conditioning period with repeated moisture content re-estimations is necessary to ensure uniformity of drying. Inherent stresses in the timber are liable to cause distortion on machining.

Kiln schedule D is recommended.

Movement

Moisture content in 90 per cent humidity	21 per cent
Moisture content in 60 per cent humidity	13 per cent
Corresponding tangential movement	2·5 per cent
Corresponding radial movement	1·7 per cent
Classification	medium movement	
Mechanical properties	Weight for weight the timber closely resembles Baltic redwood in strength properties but is marginally lower in toughness.
Resistance to insect attack	Damage by ambrosia (pinhole borer) beetles is often present. The timber is recorded as one attacked by furniture beetles (Anobiidae) in its country of origin. It is susceptible to attack by drywood termites.
Natural durability	Non-durable.
Preservative treatment	Moderately resistant. The sapwood is permeable.
Working properties	It can be worked easily by hand and machine tools and has very little dulling effect on their cutting edges. It planes and moulds to a clean, smooth finish and gives good results in most other operations. Some material is difficult to dry to a uniform moisture content and such material is liable to spring from the saw during ripsawing. The timber stains and polishes well and gives good results with paint. Saw type C or D is recommended. The timber can be glued satisfactorily.
Veneer and plywood	Logs are used for plywood manufacture in South America.
Uses	The timber is logged extensively in South America and used there for all work for which Scots pine is employed in Europe. Only the higher grades are exported to the United Kingdom. It is used for internal joinery, including doors and staircases, etc.

26

'Pencil Cedar, African'

Juniperus procera

The tree   'African pencil cedar' attains a height of 24·4–30·5 m with a diameter of 1·2–1·5 m, sometimes reaching as much as 2·4–3 m. It has a tapering trunk and heavily fluted butt. It is found in East Africa, mainly in Kenya, Uganda, Tanzania and Abyssinia, in the higher elevation forests.

The timber
—general description   Like the well-known Virginian pencil cedar (*Juniperus virginiana*), the African species is a moderately heavy, fine-textured, reddish-brown wood characterised by its 'cedar' scent and fine whittling qualities. The African timber may usually be distinguished by its less definite growth zones and the frequent presence of relatively wide bands of dense tissue contrasting with the narrow and fairly evenly spaced dark lines terminating the annual ring in the American species. The colour of the fresh timber varies from pale yellowish-brown to deep purplish-red but tones down to a more uniform reddish-brown on exposure. The average weight of the seasoned timber is about 580 kg/m³ (36 lb/cu. ft). This is slightly above the corresponding figure for the American wood.

Seasoning   This timber shows a marked tendency towards fine surface checking during seasoning. It must be considered a slow-drying species, especially in thicker sizes, with a tendency to end-splitting and checking.

Kiln schedule G is recommended.

Shrinkage

Green to 12 per cent moisture content

Tangential	3 per cent
Radial	2 per cent

Mechanical properties   Tests on a very limited amount of this timber in the unseasoned state indicated that it was about 20 per cent heavier, about 45 per cent harder, 50–60 per cent stronger in bending and in compression along the grain and 100 per cent stiffer than Virginian pencil cedar (*J. virginiana*).

Resistance to insect attack   It is said that the timber is probably immune from Bostrychid attack and the heartwood from termite attack.

Natural durability   Durable.

Preservative treatment   Extremely resistant. The sapwood is moderately resistant.

Working properties   The timber works easily in all hand and machine operations and normally has very little dulling effect on tool edges, but occasionally logs may have hard patches of a somewhat abrasive nature. It is from 15 to 20 per cent harder to cut than Virginian pencil cedar (*J. virginiana*) and is slightly more brittle. An excellent finish is obtainable in general, but cutting edges should be sharp. It is very fissile and in drilling, mortising and end moulding it must be well supported to obviate chipping. It is liable to split when nailed and requires care in screwing. The usual finishing treatments give good results. Saw type D is recommended. The timber can be glued satisfactorily.

Uses   The principal use for this timber is for slats for pencil manufacture and it has become one of the main sources of pencil slats imported into the United Kingdom. In East Africa it is employed in the joinery, furniture and carpentry trades and in the United Kingdom it has been used to a limited extent as lining for furniture.

'Pencil Cedar, Virginian'

Juniperus virginiana

Other names   'Eastern red cedar' (USA); 'pencil cedar' (Great Britain).

The tree   The tree occasionally attains a height of 30·5 m with a diameter of 0·9–1·2 m, but is usually only 12·2–15·3 m high and 0·3–0·45 m in diameter. It has a tendency, especially in old trees, to buttress at the base. The tree has a wide distribution in the eastern United States, from Maine to Georgia, and spreads westerly to a line from North Dakota to eastern Texas. In Canada it is found in southern Ontario along the St Lawrence and Ottawa rivers.

**The timber
—general description**

This is the traditional timber used for high-class pencils and is widely familiar as a fine-textured, reddish-brown wood with a characteristic 'cedar' scent and excellent whittling qualities. When freshly cut the heartwood is of a purplish- or pinkish-red colour, toning down on exposure to a more uniform reddish-brown; lighter streaks are not uncommon. The narrow sapwood is creamy white. A thin dark line of summerwood marks the boundary of each growth ring; these rings are often variable in width but material from the outer portions of old trees generally shows uniformly narrow rings. The timber now available is usually from small trees and consequently knotty; straight-grained clear stock is normally limited to pieces of very small dimension. The seasoned timber weighs about 530 kg/m³ (33 lb/cu. ft).

Mechanical properties

The species, although of similar weight to 'Douglas fir', possesses only one-half to two-thirds of its strength as a beam under static and impact loads and about half its stiffness. In hardness and resistance to splitting it possesses approximately 50 per cent higher strength values.

Resistance to insect attack

It is recorded in the West Indies as susceptible to damage by drywood termites. This 'cedar' has clothes-moth-resistant properties related to the toxicity of its volatile components to newly-hatched and young larvae.

Natural durability

Durable.

Working properties

The timber works readily with hand and machine tools and has little dulling effect on cutting edges. Straight-grained material finishes excellently if tools are sharp but disturbed grain around the fairly frequent knots tends to tear. Extra care is needed in end-grain working to prevent the wood breaking away at the tool exit. The timber gives good results with the usual finishing treatments but is liable to split when nailed. Saw type D is recommended.

Uses

The timber has a strong aroma and is used for blanket and linen chests, and also for shipbuilding, coffins and cigar boxes. Its main use is for pencil manufacture for which it is one of the best timbers available. The leaves and shavings from pencil manufacture are distilled for recovery of the essential oil present in them.

Pine, American Pitch

Principally *Pinus palustris* and *P. elliottii* (formerly confused with *P. caribaea*)

Other names

Gulf coast pitch pine, longleaf pitch pine (Great Britain); longleaf yellow pine, longleaf, southern yellow pine, southern pine (USA) (see Note, p. 29). *P. palustris* is called Florida longleaf, Florida and Georgia yellow pine; *P. elliottii* is also called slash pine.

The tree

P. palustris is generally confined to a belt of 200 kilometres deep along the Atlantic coast and the Gulf States. Its northern extremities are in south-eastern Virginia, south to Florida and along the coast to Trinity River in Texas. *P. elliottii* ranges along the coastal regions from South Carolina southward to Florida and along the Gulf States to eastern Louisiana. Both species have straight boles, growing to a height of 30·5 m with a diameter of 0·6–0·9 m.

**The timber
—general description**

The American pitch pine normally shipped to the United Kingdom is typically harder and heavier than other commercial species of pine (except for Caribbean pitch pine). As a rule the annual rings are clearly marked by the contrast between the light-coloured springwood and the darker, denser summerwood, giving the wood a somewhat coarse-textured appearance, especially in wide-ringed (quickly grown) material. The heartwood is yellowish-brown to reddish-brown, generally resinous; the lighter-coloured sapwood is variable in width according to conditions of growth, commonly about

50 mm or less in the better grades. The average weights for seasoned timber are: *Pinus palustris*, 660 kg/m³ (41 lb/cu. ft), *P. elliottii*, 690 kg/m³ (43 lb/cu. ft).

The timber of other species of southern yellow pine (as it is called in the United States), together with low-density material of *P. palustris* and *P. elliottii*, may be included in certain specifications of pitch pine (see Note below). The timber of these other species is typically lighter in weight, of coarser texture and has a wider sapwood (up to 150 mm in wide-ringed material) and is correspondingly inferior in technical properties.

Seasoning These timbers can probably be seasoned with little degrade.

Kiln schedule L is recommended.

Mechanical properties Almost identical in strength properties with imported 'Douglas fir' of similar grade. Compared with Caribbean pitch pine from British Honduras it is 5 per cent lighter in weight and, with the exception of bending and compression strengths and stiffness, has correspondingly lower strength properties.

Resistance to insect attack Damage by longhorn and Buprestid beetles is sometimes present. The timber is recorded in the West Indies as susceptible to attack by drywood termites.

Natural durability Moderately durable.

Preservative treatment Resistant. The sapwood is permeable.

Working properties The timber offers a moderate resistance to cutting with machine and hand tools and finishes cleanly in most operations. Resin is liable to be troublesome, however, through clogging cutters and teeth and adhering to machine tables and fences. In ripsawing, the amount of gum picked up by the teeth may be reduced by using saws having teeth of fairly long pitch. The timber holds nails and screws firmly and gives fairly satisfactory results with paint and other finishing treatments. Saw type D (B for the more resinous material) is recommended. The timber can be glued satisfactorily.

Uses The timber is usually marketed in the United Kingdom as American pitch pine and in the United States as longleaf yellow pine or longleaf. It is a heavy, strong timber used for shipbuilding, spars, masts, heavy constructional work, lorry and railway wagon work, exterior finish, flooring, etc. A large percentage of the rosin and turpentine of the world is produced from these species which are rich in resinous secretions.

Note The term southern yellow pine or southern pine covers the timber of several closely allied species, including *Pinus palustris* Mill. (longleaf pine), *P. elliottii* Engelm. (slash pine), *P. echinata* Mill. (shortleaf pine) and *P. taeda* L. (loblolly pine). According to the 1963 edition of the Standard Grading Rules for Southern Pine Lumber, issued by the United States Southern Pine Inspection Bureau, the term longleaf yellow pine or longleaf is restricted to the heavier, stronger material of *P. palustris* and *P. elliottii*, as defined in paragraph 7 of the Rules. Material which does not come up to this specification (formerly classified as shortleaf) is now classified as southern pine. Thus the trade name shortleaf is obsolete.

Pitch pine is the name used in the export trade and in the United Kingdom for longleaf yellow pine except in so far as specifications admit other material.

Some specifications admit *Pinus echinata*, *P. taeda*, *P. rigida* and *P. virginiana*, which are considerably lighter in weight (about 560 kg/m³ (35 lb/cu. ft), seasoned) than American pitch pine, while the light-coloured sapwood is variable in width according to the conditions of growth, up to 15·24 cm (6 in.) in wide-ringed material. Being lighter timber than American pitch pine, their strength properties are correspondingly less. Their timber is non-durable and moderately resistant to preservative treatment; the wide sapwood is permeable.

Pinus taeda has been planted extensively in the southern hemisphere, especially in South Africa, Australia and New Zealand. These plantations yield timber of much faster growth than that of the southern United States.

Pine, Austrian

Pinus nigra, var. *nigra*

Austrian pine occurs in Austria, extending into Hungary and Yugoslavia. It grows to a height of 22·9–30·5 m with a diameter of 0·9–1·2 m. It has been planted in other European countries, including Great Britain, but not extensively in the latter country except as a windbreak, the timber being usually more knotty than Scots or Corsican pine. Timber from Yugoslavia is considerably denser and more resinous than that grown in Great Britain, being somewhat similar to American pitch pine, and has been exported under the misleading name of Bosnian pitch pine. The timber is non-durable and is generally used for work such as shuttering and crates.

Pine, Canadian Red

Pinus resinosa

Other names   Norway pine (USA), red pine (Canada and USA).

The tree   Red pine grows in eastern Canada from Nova Scotia westwards to Lake St John, Central Ontario and the Winnipeg River. The southern extremities of its range are Minnesota, Wisconsin and Michigan eastwards to Pennsylvania and Massachusetts. Its height is seldom greater than 38 m and is usually from 22·9 to 30·5 m with a diameter of 0·3–0·9 m.

The timber —general description   In general character this timber is similar to Baltic redwood. The heartwood is light red or reddish-yellow and is distinct from the creamy-white sapwood, which in most logs is usually about 7·62 cm (3 in.) wide. The timber is medium to fine in texture, generally straight-grained and somewhat resinous but not sufficiently so to mar finished surfaces. The average weight is about 450 kg/m³ (28 lb/cu. ft), seasoned.

Seasoning   The timber is stated to season easily and uniformly with little checking or distortion; it is readily kiln dried and its finishing qualities are improved in the process through the setting of the resin. It shrinks in seasoning more than does yellow pine, but may be classed among the woods having medium shrinkage.

Kiln schedule L is recommended.

Mechanical properties   Red pine is a moderately light timber, about 15 per cent softer, when air-dry, than Baltic redwood (*Pinus sylvestris*), but about equal to that timber in other strength properties.

Resistance to insect attack   Damage by ambrosia (pinhole borer) beetles and by longhorn beetles is sometimes present.

Natural durability   Non-durable.

Preservative treatment   Moderately resistant. The sapwood is permeable.

Working properties   The timber works easily by hand and machine tools and does not differ greatly from Baltic redwood in working properties. It finishes cleanly and smoothly in the various operations and its knots cause little trouble in machining. The timber takes nails and screws well and reacts satisfactorily to stain, paint and other treatments. Saw type C or D is recommended. The timber can be glued satisfactorily.

Uses   It produces timber which is used for construction work, flooring, agricultural implements, etc. When treated with a preservative it is used for sleepers, poles, piles and posts. In the United States it is a source of rosin and turpentine.

Pine, Caribbean Pitch

Principally *Pinus caribaea*[1]

Other names	Caribbean longleaf, British Honduras, Bahamas, Nicaraguan pitch pine, etc., according to origin (Great Britain).
The tree	The range of this species is from the Bahamas, western Cuba, British Honduras, through Guatemala and Honduras and into Nicaragua. In the best situations it grows to 30·5 m high with a clean bole of 21·4 m and a diameter of 0·9 m. It has been planted in the northern part of New Zealand, South Africa and Australia. Except where otherwise stated the following data refer to timber from British Honduras and Nicaragua.
The timber —general description	Caribbean pitch pine resembles the American pitch pine imported from the south-eastern United States. It compares favourably with longleaf pine (the best grade of American pitch pine), being somewhat heavier on the average, about 710 kg/m³ (44 lb/cu. ft), seasoned. Timber of the same species from Nicaragua is believed to be similar, grade for grade, to the British Honduras pine. Bahamas pitch pine by comparison is typically more slowly grown (narrow ringed) and there is evidence that it is somewhat denser.
Seasoning	It requires care during seasoning and dries rather slowly. There is some tendency to split and cheek in the early stages and a marked tendency to distort later in the drying.

Kiln schedule H is advised.

Shrinkage

Green to 12 per cent moisture content

Tangential	6 per cent
Radial	3 per cent

Movement

Moisture content in 90 per cent humidity	21 per cent
Moisture content in 60 per cent humidity	13 per cent
Corresponding tangential movement	2·6 per cent
Corresponding radial movement	1·4 per cent
Classification	medium movement

Mechanical properties	Caribbean pitch pine is a dense, hard, resinous timber possessing high strength properties. When seasoned it is about 45 per cent harder than the average of American pitch pine (longleaf pine) exported to the United Kingdom from the Gulf States and 15 per cent more resistant to shock loads and to splitting. Its properties resemble very closely those of longleaf pine, the densest grade of American pitch pine.
Wood bending properties	From the small amount of material tested, this species appears to be suitable for making solid bends of moderate radii of curvature. Excessive resin exudation, however, results from the steaming treatment.

Classification	moderate

For solid bends (steamed)

R/S (supported)	14
R/S (unsupported)	28

Resistance to insect attack	Damage by ambrosia (pinhole borer) beetles is occasionally present.
Natural durability	Moderately durable.
Preservative treatment	Moderately resistant, varying with resin content. The sapwood is permeable.
Working properties	The working properties of Caribbean pitch pine are similar to those of American pitch pine from the United States, but it is generally a little heavier and slightly more

[1] *Pinus oocarpa* (ocote pine) may be included in consignments of Caribbean pitch pine from certain localities. It is known to have been shipped from the west coast of Nicaragua. It appears to be similar to longleaf pine in general character and properties.

31

resinous than the latter timber. Owing to the high resin content, the ease and steadiness of feeding is affected in some operations by resin adhering to tool edges, machine tables and fences. It has a fairly small blunting effect on cutting edges, although a faster rate of blunting is likely to occur during prolonged runs with clogged teeth and cutters. Some relief from the effect of the resin may be obtained in sawing by the use of saws having a fairly long tooth pitch. Clear material planes cleanly but at the higher rates of feed careful setting and jointing of the cutters are necessary to minimise tearing around knots. The timber may sometimes split in nailing although, in general, it holds nails well. Saw type D is recommended (B for the more resinous material). The timber can be glued satisfactorily.

Uses   The timber is used for vat making and in the boat-building industry for decking, masts, spars and temporary bulkheads. It is often seen as panelling and interior joinery in old buildings. Imports into the United Kingdom are in baulks or sawn sizes.

Pine, Corsican

Pinus nigra subsp. *laricio* (*P. nigra* var. *calabria*)

The tree   Corsican pine has a wide distribution in the Mediterranean area, being found in Spain, Italy, Greece and extending into southern Russia. It is also found in pure forests on Corsica and Sicily. It was introduced into Great Britain, where it has been planted extensively. It has also been planted in New Zealand where it grows quickly. It attains a height of 45·7 m and a diameter of 1·5 m, but the latter usually is not greater than 0·9 m. Except where otherwise stated the following information refers to timber grown in plantations in Great Britain.

The timber —general description   The timber grown in this country is in general similar to Scots pine, but has a larger proportion of sapwood and is usually somewhat coarser in texture. The average weight of the seasoned timber is about 510 kg/m³ (32 lb/cu. ft); in the green condition (130 per cent moisture content) it is about 930 kg/m³ (58 lb/cu. ft).

The timber grown in Corsica appears to be generally of finer texture than home-grown Corsican pine and, apart from a greater prevalence of large knots, fairly comparable with the general run of Baltic redwood.

Seasoning   This timber seasons very rapidly and well without much degrade, though knots may split and some resin exudation may occur. Owing to the liability of the sapwood of the green timber to develop blue stain, no time should be lost between conversion and loading into the kilns for drying.

Kiln schedule M is recommended.

Shrinkage

Green to 12 per cent moisture content

Tangential	5·5 per cent
Radial	3 per cent

Movement

Moisture content in 90 per cent humidity	19 per cent
Moisture content in 60 per cent humidity	12·5 per cent
Corresponding tangential movement	1·6 per cent
Corresponding radial movement	0·9 per cent
Classification	small movement

Mechanical properties   The seasoned timber is about 20 per cent more difficult to split along the rings (tangentially) than Baltic redwood. In other strength properties the differences between the two timbers grade for grade are not sufficiently marked to be of any practical importance. Round timber in pole and post size consisting of the wood put on in early growth, which is considerably faster grown than that of similar wood in Scots pine, is therefore weaker in bending strength and more brittle. Limited tests in the green condition on material of this species from Corsica suggest that the density and strength are appreciably superior to those of the home-grown material.

32

Resistance to insect attack	The timber is susceptible to attack by the common furniture beetle.
Natural durability	Non-durable.
Preservative treatment	Moderately resistant. This timber contains a large amount of permeable sapwood.
Working properties	The timber generally works well with most hand and machine tools, if sharp cutting edges are employed. The working properties of Corsican pine are very similar to those of Scots pine, except that the knots of the former are slightly less hard and usually hold better during cutting. The timber nails fairly well and responds satisfactorily to the usual finishing treatments. Saw type C or D is recommended.
Uses	The timber is used for the same purposes as Scots pine. For those where deep impregnation with preservative is needed, this timber is very suitable owing to its thick permeable sapwood. The old trees in Corsica produce some very fine close-grown timber which is comparable to the southern United States pitch pine and is used for high-class joinery.

Pine, Jack

Pinus banksiana

Other name	Princess pine (Canada).
The tree	Jack pine is mainly found in Canada from Nova Scotia through Quebec to Manitoba and then northwards to the Mackenzie River Valley. It is also found in the United States in Indiana and certain parts of Michigan. On its optimum sites it grows to 24·4 m but usually it is 15·3 m with a diameter of 0·3 m.
The timber —general description	This timber is of the hard pine class, similar in appearance and general character to Canadian red pine or Baltic redwood. It is, however, inclined to be knotty and is available only in relatively small sizes. The pale sapwood is narrow, usually less than 50 mm in width; the heartwood varies in colour from pale brown to reddish-brown. The timber weighs about 500 kg/m³ (31 lb/cu. ft), seasoned.
Seasoning	This species is stated to season without difficulty and with little degrade; shrinkage is said to be comparatively small. Kiln schedule L is advised.
Mechanical properties	The strength properties of jack pine are practically identical with those of Baltic redwood.
Natural durability	Non-durable.
Preservative treatment	Moderately resistant. The sapwood is permeable.
Working properties	The timber is somewhat variable in texture and weight, but the better material is comparable with Canadian red pine in working properties. It is generally a little coarser, more brittle and resinous than the latter and does not finish quite so cleanly and smoothly. It works easily by hand and machine tools, and to a reasonably good finish when sharp tools are employed. The timber takes nails and screws well, stains effectively and gives good results with paint and varnish provided that resinous material is well dried before use. Saw type C or D is recommended.
Uses	This species is becoming increasingly important as lumber in Canada. As it takes creosote well it is used as sleepers, poles, etc. It is exported mixed with white spruce and balsam fir, is used as pulpwood for the kraft pulp mills and cut for pitprops.

33

Pine, Lodgepole

Pinus contorta (*P. contorta* var. *latifolia*)

Other name   Contorta pine (Great Britain).

The tree   It is a tree of the western coastal areas of North America, ranging from the Yukon to the eastern Rockies through Montana and Colorado. It is found in the Sierra Nevada mountains as high as 2745 m. The tree is usually found at 610–1830 m, where it forms dense stands, developing a slender trunk 15·3–30·5 m high with a diameter of 0·3–0·6 m. In Great Britain this species has been planted to some extent in Wales and Scotland and it is also grown in other parts of Europe, but as yet little is known about the quality of plantation-grown timber; the following information refers to the North American timber unless otherwise stated. Plantations in the southern hemisphere have been established over a considerable acreage.

The timber —general description   A pale-coloured timber having heartwood which is often little darker than the narrow sapwood. It is soft, straight-grained and of fine, fairly even texture, rather similar to ponderosa pine in this respect. Small, tight knots are a common feature and the dimpled appearance of the split tangential surface is also characteristic. The average weight of the seasoned timber is about 470 kg/m³ (29 lb/cu. ft).

Seasoning   From a small-scale test on home-grown material this timber appears to season very rapidly and well with no checking or splitting. Distortion is mainly slight although moderate twist sometimes occurs, and resin exudation is fairly general.

Kiln schedule L is advised.

Shrinkage

Green to 12 per cent moisture content
Tangential	4 per cent
Radial	2·6 per cent

Movement

Moisture content in 90 per cent humidity	19 per cent
Moisture content in 60 per cent humidity	12 per cent
Corresponding tangential movement	1·6 per cent
Corresponding radial movement	0·8 per cent
Classification	small movement

Mechanical properties   This species has somewhat similar strength properties to Baltic redwood.

Resistance to insect attack   Damage by ambrosia (pinhole borer) beetles, longhorn and Buprestid beetles is sometimes present.

Natural durability   Non-durable.

Preservative treatment   Resistant.

Working properties   The timber works easily with machine and hand tools but resin exudation may sometimes be troublesome. Clear material has little dulling effect and that caused by the knots is not unduly severe, as they are usually sound. It finishes cleanly, takes nails satisfactorily and gives fairly good results with paint. Saw type C or D is recommended. The timber can be glued satisfactorily.

Uses   Lodgepole pine is extensively used on the eastern slopes of the Rockies and is one of the principal species in that area. It is used primarily for railway sleepers, mining timbers, transmission and telegraph poles and fencing and is a valuable species in the manufacture of pulp.

Pine, Maritime

Pinus pinaster

The tree   Maritime pine is a native of the Mediterranean region. It is usually confined to the coastal region, from Greece to the shores of the Atlantic in France and Portugal. It has been extensively planted in France in the Landes and in Portugal and to a small extent on sandy coastal areas in Great Britain. The tree attains a height of 36·6 m and a diameter of 0·9–1·2 m.

The timber —general description

This timber is roughly comparable to Scots pine but tends to be more resinous, and when produced under conditions favourable to rapid growth is generally coarser, knottier and has a larger proportion of sapwood. In western Europe it is an important resin-producing species and much of the timber is obtained from trees which have been tapped for resin. This process induces the production of considerable quantities of resin, some of which remains in the timber giving it an appearance reminiscent of resinous grades of pitch pine. The seasoned timber varies a good deal in weight according to the resin content; when this is low the weight is near that of Scots pine (510 kg/m³ (32 lb/cu. ft)), but very resinous material is commonly some 16–24 kg/m³ (10–15 lb/cu. ft) heavier than this.

Seasoning

Kiln schedule M is recommended.

Shrinkage

Green to 12 per cent moisture content

Tangential	4·5 per cent
Radial	2 per cent

Mechanical properties

This species is similar in weight to home-grown Scots pine and possesses corresponding strength properties.

Resistance to insect attack

Damage by ambrosia (pinhole borer) beetles, longhorn beetles and wood-wasps (*Sirex* spp.) is sometimes present. The wood is susceptible to attack by the common furniture beetle.

Natural durability

Moderately durable.

Preservative treatment

Resistant. The sapwood, which comprises a large part of the timber, is permeable.

Working properties

The timber generally works readily with machine and hand tools and finishes cleanly provided that sharp cutters are used. The dulling effect on tool edges is normally small but resin, especially in the denser grades of material, may cause accelerated blunting through clogging teeth and cutters. This trouble may be minimised in sawing by using teeth having a fairly long pitch. Saw type D for normal material is recommended; saw type B for resinous material.

Uses

In France and Portugal the trees are cut for timber and used for building construction, railway work, etc. Material exported to Great Britain is used for pallets, for box and packing-case manufacture and pitprops. In France and Portugal the trees are tapped for resin. Kraft paper has been made from maritime pine in France.

Pine, Ponderosa

Pinus ponderosa

Other names

British Columbia soft pine (Canada); western yellow, Californian white pine (USA).

The tree

Ponderosa pine has a large range, from the North Thompson River in British Columbia southwards through Montana, western Nebraska and Texas and into Mexico and westwards to the Pacific coast. Ordinarily it attains a height of 30·5 m and a diameter of 0·6–0·76 m but under optimum conditions it grows to 48·8–51·9 m and 1·2 m diameter. It is not found on swampy land but on sandy soil or well-drained slopes up to 1525 m altitude. It has been planted extensively in New Zealand, being the next most-planted species to *P. radiata* in that country. It has been planted in Australia and South Africa to a lesser extent. The following information refers to the natural forest-grown timber of British Columbia and the United States.

35

The timber **—general description**	The wood varies widely in appearance and general properties. Mature trees have a very thick, pale yellow sapwood, soft, non-resinous and uniform in texture, approaching yellow pine and western white pine in quality, but slightly heavier than these. The heartwood is much darker, varying from a deep yellow to a reddish-brown, and is considerably heavier than the sapwood. The average weight for the species is about 510 kg/m³ (32 lb/cu. ft), seasoned, that is, about the same as Baltic redwood. Resin ducts are fairly prominent on longitudinal surfaces, especially in the heartwood, as fine, dark brown lines. This species occasionally shows a dimpled appearance on tangential surfaces.
Seasoning	It is stated that the timber seasons readily, though care must be exercised in air seasoning on account of the susceptibility of the sapwood to blue staining if not properly piled on a suitable site. Kiln schedule L is recommended.
Mechanical properties	Canadian-grown ponderosa pine is about 20 per cent more resistant to splitting along the rings than Baltic redwood, but otherwise differs very little from that timber in mechanical properties. Timber grown in the United States is on the average about 15–20 per cent lighter and proportionately inferior in mechanical properties to that grown in Canada.
Resistance to insect attack	Damage by ambrosia (pinhole borer) beetles, longhorn and Buprestid beetles is occasionally present. The timber is recorded in the West Indies as susceptible to attack by drywood termites.
Natural durability	Non-durable.
Preservative treatment	Moderately resistant. The sapwood is permeable.
Working properties	The timber works easily in all hand and machine operations; clear material has very little dulling effect and that caused by the knots is not unduly severe, as they are usually sound. It finishes cleanly, takes nails well and gives fairly good results in painting, etc., but resin exudation is sometimes troublesome, more especially with timber from butt logs. Saw type C or D is recommended. The timber can be glued satisfactorily.
Uses	It is a valuable source of material for boxes and packing cases in British Columbia. The sapwood yields a fine quality timber, similar to that of yellow pine (*Pinus strobus*), and is used in America for pattern making and other purposes for which stability is important. The timber is also used for building, general carpentry and, when treated with a preservative, for sleepers, poles and posts.

Pine, Radiata

Pinus radiata (P. insignis)

Other names	Insignis pine (general); insignis (South Africa); Monterey pine (USA).
The tree	The natural distribution of this species is limited to a narrow belt on the southern Californian coast. Large acreages have been planted in the southern hemisphere, mainly in New Zealand, Australia and South Africa. In its natural habitat the tree grows to 15·3–18·3 m, sometimes reaching as much as 30·5 m with a diameter of 0·3–0·6 m. In the southern hemisphere it grows fast, reaching a height of 21·4–24·4 m in 25–30 years. Except where otherwise stated the following information refers to plantation timber as grown in the southern hemisphere.
The timber **—general description**	Like Corsican pine this species is characterised by a wide, pale-coloured sapwood, commonly 75–150 mm in width, distinct from the pinkish-brown heartwood. The growth rings, although mostly wide and distinct, show rather less contrast between the springwood and summerwood than those of other hard pines such as Scots or Corsican

pine, and in consequence the texture is relatively uniform. Resin ducts appear on the longitudinal surfaces as fine brown lines. The average weight of the seasoned timber is about 480 kg/m³ (30 lb/cu. ft).

Seasoning It is stated that this timber seasons with little degrade if reasonable care is taken. In timber from immature trees, however, spiral grain may cause appreciable warping accentuated by distortion of grain around knots. Weighting of the kiln stack and steaming of the load under weight for several hours has been carried out to reduce distortion.

Kiln schedule K is recommended.

Shrinkage

Shrinkage from green to 12 per cent moisture content is stated to be

Tangential	4 per cent
Radial	2·5 per cent

Movement

Moisture content in 90 per cent humidity	20 per cent
Moisture content in 60 per cent humidity	12·5 per cent
Corresponding tangential movement	2 per cent
Corresponding radial movement	1·2 per cent
Classification	medium movement

Resistance to insect attack Damage by ambrosia (pinhole borer) beetles and by longhorn beetles is occasionally present. The timber is recorded in New Zealand as susceptible to attack by the common furniture beetle, *Anobium punctatum*.

Natural durability Non-durable.

Preservative treatment The bulk of the timber available is the product of comparatively young rapidly grown plantation trees and consists almost entirely of permeable sapwood.

Working properties The timber works a little more easily than Corsican pine, and clear material has very little dulling effect on cutting edges. Apart from tearing around knots, it planes to a smooth, clean finish provided that cutters having sharp, thin edges are used. Dull, or thickened, cutters tend to tear the wide zones of soft springwood. Saw type C or D is recommended. The timber can be glued satisfactorily.

Uses The timber is used for joinery, building, crates and boxes and general construction and some is exported. In New Zealand it is also made into pulp for kraft and newsprint paper.

Pine, Scots or Redwood[1]

Pinus sylvestris

Other names 'Fir', 'Norway fir', 'Scots fir', red pine, red deal or 'red', yellow deal or 'yellow', Baltic/Finnish/Swedish/Archangel/Siberian/Polish redwood or yellow deal, etc., according to origin (Great Britain).

The tree The tree has an extraordinarily wide distribution, ranging from Spain into the Arctic Circle and on almost all geological formations. Its northerly limits are on the north-west coast of Norway at Alten, spreading east through northern Europe into Asia. In Siberia it does not reach the Arctic Circle. Its eastern extreme is about 150°E longitude in the Werchojansk Mountains. In the east its southern limits extend to Upper Amur and in Europe it is found in the Caucasus and Transylvanian Alps. It extends through

---

[1] In accordance with established custom, timber of this species imported from the Continent of Europe is commonly called redwood, red deal, or simply 'red' (especially in the North), and yellow deal or 'yellow' (especially in the South), while timber grown in the British Isles is generally known as Scots pine. Names indicating the geographical origin of imported timber, e.g. Finnish redwood, Swedish redwood, may be used as alternatives to the basic standard name redwood.

the Maritime Alps in France and reaches the eastern Pyrenees. In Spain it reaches the Sierra Nevada in Andalusia, which is its extreme southerly point. The westerly limits are the mountains of Avila, in Spain, and Great Britain.

The tree is commonly 30·5 m, sometimes reaching 39·6–42·7 m in height with a diameter of 0·6–0·9 m and sometimes reaching 1·2 m.

The timber —general description

The extensive geographical range of this species embraces a wide variation in growth conditions which in turn is reflected in the variable character of the timber, particularly in regard to its texture, density and the number and size of knots. In the seasoned condition the pale reddish-brown resinous heartwood is usually distinct from the lighter-coloured sapwood. In home-grown Scots pine the sapwood is usually 50–100 mm in width; in imported Baltic redwood it may be considerably less, particularly in slowly grown timber from the more northerly regions. Annual rings are clearly marked by the contrasting light springwood and darker summerwood zones. The weight of the seasoned timber averages about 510 kg/m³ (32 lb/cu. ft); in the green condition (85 per cent moisture content) it is about 800 kg/m³ (50 lb/cu. ft).

Seasoning

This timber seasons very rapidly and well. Owing to its tendency to blue stain, the wood, if not dipped in a solution of sap-stain preventative, should be loaded into the kiln with as little delay as possible.

Kiln schedule M is recommended, or if colour is important, schedule F.

Shrinkage

Green to 12 per cent moisture content

Tangential	4·5 per cent
Radial	3 per cent

Movement

Moisture content in 90 per cent humidity	20 per cent
Moisture content in 60 per cent humidity	12·5 per cent
Corresponding tangential movement	2·1 per cent
Corresponding radial movement	0·9 per cent
Classification	medium movement

Mechanical properties

	Moisture content	Bending strength		Modulus of elasticity		Compression parallel to grain		Impact (toughness) max drop of hammer	
		N/mm²	lbf/in.²	N/mm²	1 000 lbf/in.²	N/mm²	lbf/in.²	m	in.
United Kingdom	Green	46	6 700	7 300	1 060	21·9	3 180	0·69	27
	12 per cent	89	12 900	10 000	1 450	47·4	6 870	0·71	28
European	Green	44	6 400	7 700	1 120	21·0	3 050	0·69	27
	12·8 per cent	83	1 200	10 000	1 450	45·0	6 530	0·66	26

The home-grown timber is, when seasoned, about 20 per cent harder on the side grain than the imported material, and 15–30 per cent more difficult to split.

Resistance to insect attack

Damage by ambrosia (pinhole borer) beetles and by longhorn beetles is sometimes present. The wood is susceptible to attack by the common furniture beetle.

Natural durability

Non-durable.

Preservative treatment

Moderately resistant. The sapwood is permeable.

Working properties

The working properties of the timber depend to a large extent upon the rate of growth and knottiness. Whilst the heavier grades of material produced in this country offer a moderate resistance to cutting and may present a little difficulty through resin adhering to the tools, the timber generally works easily and cleanly in most hand and machine operations. Knots are, however, sometimes troublesome when dried, as they are liable to become loose and to fall out in planing and sawing. In comparison with imported material, there is a little more need for maintaining sharp, thin cutting edges on tools when working the home-grown timber; the latter is usually of rather faster growth, and thus its wider bands of soft springwood have slightly more tendency to tear up if machined with dull cutters. Scots pine and Baltic redwood take nails well, can be stained effectively and give good results with paint, varnish and polish. Saw type C (D for the heavier material) is recommended. The timber can generally be glued satisfactorily but is sometimes troublesome if it is very resinous.

Veneer and plywood This species is used in northern Europe for the manufacture of plywood.

Uses The timber is used for all kinds of constructional work. The better grades are employed for joinery, furniture and turnery while the general run of timber is used for general building purposes. Large quantities were used annually for sleepers in railway work as the sapwood takes preservatives easily. In the round it is used for telegraph poles, piles and pitprops, the first two usually being treated beforehand. It is employed in the chemical wood pulp industry. There are few timber-using industries that do not employ this species for some purpose.

Generally speaking, the further north the timber is grown the slower the growth. Slow-growth timber is favoured for joinery, whereas more vigorous growth timber is commonly used for carcassing. Scots pine grown in Britain can be used in the same way provided that it is properly sawn, seasoned and graded. The general run of sawn timber from well-managed woodlands is suitable for building and general purposes. The clear narrow-ringed wood found in large mature trees is of excellent quality for joinery but this is only a small proportion of the total production.

Pine, Western White

Pinus monticola

Other name Idaho white pine (USA).

The tree Western white pine is scattered through the mountain forest from the Columbia River in British Columbia south into California to the Kern River. The eastern extremity of its distribution is in the north part of Montana and it is most abundant in northern Idaho. It is found from sea level up to 3050 m elevation.

The timber —general description A light, straight-grained, even-textured wood having heartwood mostly of a pale straw colour, only slightly darker than the white sapwood (which is generally between 25 and 75 mm wide), but varying to shades of reddish-brown; fine dark brown lines (resin ducts) are to be seen on longitudinal surfaces. Little contrast is apparent between the springwood and summerwood zones. Compared with yellow pine, western white pine has, on the average, rather narrower growth rings and is slightly heavier, weighing about 420 kg/m³ (26 lb/cu. ft), seasoned.

Seasoning It is stated that this timber seasons with little checking or warping and that it shrinks slightly more than yellow pine during drying.

Kiln schedule L is recommended.

Mechanical properties Western white pine is, on the whole, stronger than yellow pine, its superiority being rather more marked after seasoning than before. Thus, the air-dry timber is 30 per cent harder and stiffer than yellow pine, 25 per cent more resistant to shock loads, 25 per cent stronger in compression along the grain and 15 per cent stronger in bending. Its resistance to splitting is the same as that of yellow pine.

Resistance to insect attack Damage by ambrosia (pinhole borer) beetles, longhorn and Buprestid beetles is sometimes present. The timber is recorded in the West Indies as susceptible to attack by drywood termites.

Natural durability Non-durable.

Preservative treatment Moderately resistant. The sapwood is permeable.

39

Working properties	The timber works very easily by hand and machine tools and has little dulling effect on their cutting edges. It is closely similar to yellow pine in working properties but it is very slightly less easy to cut than the latter. It finishes excellently in most operations provided that the cutters are reasonably sharp. It has good nailing and screwing properties, takes stain readily and paints, varnishes and polishes well. Saw type C or D is recommended. The timber can be glued satisfactorily.
Veneer and plywood	Logs are used in the United States and Canada for the manufacture of plywood.
Uses	The wood is similar to yellow pine and is also used for pattern making, interior joinery, etc.

Pine, Yellow

Pinus strobus

Other names	White, cork, Weymouth, pattern, sapling, pumpkin, Quebec pine.
The tree	The tree is a native of North America and occurs from Newfoundland west to the Manitoba border. It is found to the south of the Great Lakes in Iowa, Illinois and Indiana and along the Appalachian Mountains through eastern Kentucky and Tennessee into northern Georgia. Under favourable conditions it sometimes reaches 45·7 m in height and 1·5 m in diameter, but in the average stand it is rarely found over 30·5 m in height or more than 0·6–0·9 m in diameter.
The timber —general description	It is a soft, straight-grained and very even-textured wood with inconspicuous growth rings. The heartwood is a pale straw colour to light reddish-brown, usually little darker than the whitish sapwood. The wood is not particularly resinous, but resin ducts may generally be distinguished on longitudinal surfaces as fine short lines. Second-growth timber is of coarser texture and tends to be knotty and cross-grained. The average weight is about 390 kg/m³ (24 lb/cu. ft), seasoned.
Seasoning	A most important characteristic of this timber is its low shrinkage, and in this respect it is superior to all other Canadian timbers except the cedars. It is stated to season easily and uniformly, though care has to be exercised to prevent staining, especially of the sapwood.
	If brown stain can be tolerated, kiln schedule L would appear to be suitable. To avoid brown stain developing during kiln drying, both temperatures and relative humidities should be kept lower and the greatest possible ventilation given during the early stages of drying. At least 65·5°C, however, is necessary to set the resin.

Shrinkage

Green to 12 per cent moisture content

Tangential	3·5 per cent
Radial	1·5 per cent

Movement

Moisture content in 90 per cent humidity	20 per cent
Moisture content in 60 per cent humidity	12 per cent
Corresponding tangential movement	1·8 per cent
Corresponding radial movement	0·9 per cent
Classification	small movement

Mechanical properties	Yellow pine is a lighter, softer and weaker timber than Baltic redwood. When seasoned it is 45 per cent softer, 30 per cent weaker in bending and in compression along the grain, 25 per cent less resistant to shock loads and 20 per cent less stiff and less resistant to splitting.
Resistance to insect attack	Damage by ambrosia (pinhole borer) beetles and longhorn beetles is occasionally present. It is also susceptible to attack by the common furniture beetle, *Anobium punctatum*, and has been recorded in the West Indies as susceptible to attack by drywood termites.

40

Natural durability	Non-durable.
Preservative treatment	Moderately resistant. The sapwood is permeable.
Working properties	The timber works very easily by hand and machine tools and has little dulling effect on their cutting edges. It finishes excellently in most operations, cutting well both with and across the grain, provided that the cutters are reasonably sharp, for being soft it tends to crumble slightly under dulled edges. It has good nailing and screwing properties and takes stain, paint, polish, etc., readily and well. Saw type C or D is recommended.
Uses	This species produces the most valuable softwood timber in North America. The outstanding use is for pattern stock or similar uses where soft, easily worked, even-textured material is required. It is also employed in cabinet making, interior finishing of buildings and for woodware.

Podo

Podocarpus gracilior, P. milanjianus, P. usambarensis and *P. ensiculus*[1]

Other name	Yellowwood (South Africa).
The tree	These species grow to a height of 30·5 m or more, with diameters averaging 0·45–0·76 m, though *P. gracilior* is sometimes of very large diameter. It occurs at altitudes of 1220–2745 m in Kenya, Uganda and Abyssinia and has also been recorded in Tanzania. *P. milanjianus* is widely distributed in Kenya at altitudes of 2135–3050 m and is also found in Uganda and southward through parts of Tanzania to Nyasaland and Rhodesia. *P. usambarensis* grows at lower altitudes in Kenya and Tanzania.
The timber —general description	The East African species of *Podocarpus* are very similar so far as their timber is concerned and are indiscriminately mixed for most practical purposes. The timber differs from that of the typical European softwoods in having no clearly defined growth rings; consequently it has a more uniform texture. It is classed as non-resinous and is quite odourless. It is generally straight-grained. The weight is similar to that of Baltic redwood, namely about 510 kg/m³ (32 lb/cu. ft), seasoned. As a rule it is of a uniform, light yellowish-brown colour throughout with no clear distinction between sapwood and heartwood, but some logs show a small darker-coloured core.
Seasoning	The timber seasons fairly rapidly but has a pronounced tendency to distort and some inclination to check and split. It is recommended that the timber pile should be weighted and distortion restrained mechanically so far as is possible. The wood often shrinks appreciably in the longitudinal direction owing to the presence of compression wood.
	Kiln schedule A is recommended.

Shrinkage

Green to 12 per cent moisture content

Tangential	4 per cent
Radial	2·5 per cent

Mechanical properties	From the results of strength tests carried out on somewhat limited samples, there do not appear to be any marked differences in strength between the three species. On the average they are about 50 per cent harder than Baltic redwood, but about equal to that timber in other strength properties.
Wood bending properties	Tests carried out on a small amount of material of three species of podo have indicated that the timber is suitable for solid bends of moderate radii of curvature. *P. milanjianus*

[1] This species, recognised in Tanzania in 1954, is believed to be the source of a substantial proportion of the timber hitherto regarded as that of the allied *P. milanjianus*.

41

appears to be slightly superior to either of the other two species, *P. gracilior* and *P. usambarensis*.

Classification	moderate

For solid bends (steamed)

P. gracilior and *P. usambarensis*	
R/S (supported)	18
R/S (unsupported)	20
P. milanjianus	
R/S (supported)	10
R/S (unsupported)	16

For thin laminae (unsteamed)
No data are available.

Resistance to insect attack Logs are occasionally attacked by ambrosia (pinhole borer) beetles. Trees and timber are susceptible to infestation by the longhorn beetle, *Oemida gahani*, a pest prevalent in Kenya.

There are a few records of damage by powder-post beetles (*Bostrychidae* and *Lyctidae*).

Natural durability Non-durable.

Preservative treatment Permeable.

Working properties The timber works easily by hand and machine tools and has little dulling effect on their cutting edges. In comparison with American whitewood, *P. milanjianus* offers about the same resistance to cutting whereas *P. gracilior* is 15 per cent and *P. usambarensis* 25 per cent easier to cut. Material from all three species planes and moulds to a good finish, and turns well. It gives satisfactory results in other operations if reasonable care is taken to prevent breaking away at the exit of the tool when cutting across the grain, in boring, mortising, end moulding, etc., as the timber is inclined to be brittle. It has a tendency to split in nailing unless thin gauge nails are used, but holds screws firmly. Podo stains readily but not always uniformly; it takes varnish, paint and polish well. Saw type D is recommended. The timber can be glued satisfactorily.

Veneer and plywood It is reported that *P. gracilior* is suitable for good grade plywood and *P. milanjianus* for cores and low-grade plywood.

Uses Podo is used for joinery and interior fittings and as a general utility softwood where durability is not of major importance.

'Port Orford Cedar'

Chamaecyparis lawsoniana

Other name Lawson's cypress (Great Britain).

The tree 'Port Orford cedar' attains a height of 61 m and frequently a diameter of 3·7 m above the large swollen base. It has a very limited range along the coast of southern Oregon to California and seldom extends inland farther than 48 kilometres. It has been planted to some extent in Great Britain but can be considered as only a secondary species here. Information given below relates to timber grown in North America except where otherwise stated.

The timber
—general description This timber has a fine even texture and a characteristic fragrant, spicy odour. The heartwood is of a pale pinkish-brown colour, barely distinct from the lighter-coloured sapwood. Although the timber is typically non-resinous, slight orange-yellow exudations are occasionally seen.

The weight is about 470 kg/m³ (29 lb/cu. ft), seasoned.

The imported timber is usually slower grown than that grown in Great Britain, but clear material of home-grown timber is similar in general character to imported

42

material of moderate growth rate. Its average weight is probably a little lower, say, 430 kg/m³ (27 lb/cu. ft), seasoned.

Seasoning	This timber can probably be seasoned with little degrade.
	Kiln schedule J is recommended.
Mechanical properties	The strength properties of this species are only slightly below those of coast type 'Douglas fir' although its weight is only seven-eighths of that of the latter timber.
Wood bending properties	Considerable variation in the bending properties of this species is likely to be encountered. In general it cannot be bent appreciably without severe buckling and fibre rupture occurring. No advantage appears to be gained by using a supporting strap and the species may be said to be useless for most steam bending purposes.

Classification	very poor
For solid bends (*steamed*)	
R/S (supported)	34
R/S (unsupported)	18
For thin laminae (*unsteamed*)	
R/S	59

Resistance to insect attack	Damage by longhorn beetles and *Sirex* is sometimes present.
Natural durability	Durable.
Preservative treatment	Moderately resistant. The sapwood is permeable.
Working properties	The timber works easily with all hand and machine tools. It has very little dulling effect on cutting edges and finishes cleanly in most operations. Home-grown material sometimes has a tendency to tear in planing and moulding, for it is usually faster grown than the same species grown in the United States and the grain may be wavy. The timber takes nails and screws well and gives good results with paints, stains and polishes. Saw type C or D is recommended.
Uses	In North America it is used for ship and boat building, canoe paddles, furniture and cabinet work and organ pipes. On the Pacific coast it is extensively used for match manufacture.

Sequoia

Sequoia sempervirens

Other names	Californian redwood, redwood (USA).
The tree	A tree which grows to 61–104 m in height with a diameter of 3–4·6 m. A diameter of up to 8·5 m at the heavily buttressed base has been recorded. Its northern limits are the Chilio River in southern Oregon, where it extends southwards near the coast to Monterey county, California. It is rarely found more than 32–48 kilometres from the coast, beyond the influence of the ocean fogs, or above 915 m elevation. It has been planted in Great Britain only in small clumps, where it grows fast and produces a very light-weight timber.
	The information below relates to timber from California unless otherwise stated.
The timber —general description	The timber of this species imported from California as Californian redwood is typically reddish-brown, straight-grained and light in weight, resembling western red cedar in general character. It has a similar growth ring figure, produced by the contrasting shades of the summerwood and springwood zones, but is brighter in colour and a little heavier. Like western red cedar, the timber is classed as non-resinous but it also lacks odour and is non-tainting. The near-white sapwood is very narrow. In quality the timber varies, much of it being of fine, even texture, but some is coarser and heavier with more conspicuous hard summerwood zones. The average weight of the seasoned timber is about 420 kg/m³ (26 lb/cu. ft).

43

The timber grown in this country is usually lighter in weight and coarser in texture than that imported from California and, being derived largely from ornamental trees, is generally of inferior quality.

Seasoning

Kiln schedule K is recommended.

Mechanical properties

The timber is lighter than Baltic redwood and slightly weaker in all its strength properties.

Resistance to insect attack

Logs are occasionally attacked by longhorn beetles and ambrosia (pinhole borer) beetles.

Natural durability

Durable.

Preservative treatment

Moderately resistant based on home-grown material.

Working properties

The timber works easily in all hand and machine operations and has very little dulling effect on tools. A good finish is generally obtainable provided that sharp cutters are used. The material splinters rather easily and some care is necessary to prevent breaking away at the tool exit during end-grain working. It is subject to chip-bruising in planing and moulding and to alleviate this difficulty the waste removal system must be efficient and the cutters should be honed free of all wire edge. The timber takes and holds nails fairly well and gives good results with paint and the usual finishing treatments. Saw type C is recommended. The timber can be glued satisfactorily but stains readily with alkaline adhesives.

Veneer and plywood

The timber is used in the western United States for the manufacture of plywood.

Uses

Because of its durability it can be used in exposed situations, and in California it is used for the construction of wooden pipes, flumes and work in contact with the ground. In North America it is used for vat making, particularly in situations where resistance to decay is required. It is a very useful timber for interior and exterior joinery and has also been employed extensively in organ building, especially for the pipes. The bark and offcuts from the sawmills are used for making fibreboard.

The bark, which is often 225 mm or more thick, contains a long stringy fibre, and has certain specialised applications, for example, in making sheet material for special purposes, filtering media, etc.

'Southern Cypress'

Taxodium distichum

Other names

'Louisiana cypress', 'Gulf cypress' and 'swamp cypress' (USA).

The tree

The tree is 30·5–36·6 m tall with a 1·2–1·5 m diameter above the enlarged strongly buttressed and usually hollow base. It is found in swampy areas and on the banks of streams. The northern limits in the United States are from New Jersey, west through the southern part of Indiana, Illinois and south-eastern Missouri. Its westerly limits are in the State of Texas and it is found along the Gulf States and in Florida.

The timber —general description

The colour of the timber varies from pale yellowish-brown to dark reddish-brown or almost black, timber from the coastal swamps being characteristically darker in colour and having narrower sapwood than that from inland. The darker colour is associated with better development of the summerwood zones and wood of this kind, known as red cypress, is denser and reputedly more durable; it is frequently sold separately from the lighter-coloured white or yellow cypress. In all kinds of 'southern cypress' there is usually a marked contrast in colour between springwood and summerwood zones and this gives rise to a distinct growth ring figure, particularly on flat-sawn surfaces. Darker resin streaks are often just discernible in the springwood zones. The wood is commonly rather greasy to the touch and may have a sour odour, especially in the case

44

of darker-coloured stock, but the wood does not appear to cause tainting. The grain is typically straight. The average weight of the seasoned timber is about 510 kg/m³ (32 lb/cu. ft).

Seasoning This timber is stated to season well but has been found to be very refractory in thick dimensions.

Kiln schedule K is recommended.

Mechanical properties 'Southern cypress' is slightly heavier than Baltic redwood but has very similar strength properties.

Resistance to insect attack Logs are occasionally attacked by longhorn beetles.

Natural durability Durable.

Preservative treatment Moderately resistant.

Working properties The timber works easily and finishes cleanly in most operations, provided that sharp tools are employed. In planing and moulding, particularly of fast-grown material, dull cutters have a tendency to cause grain raising. The timber takes nails well and has good painting properties. Saw type C is recommended. The timber can be glued satisfactorily.

Uses The timber is used in the United States for construction, fencing, sleepers and cooperage. It also gives very good performance as chemical tanks and vats. It is suitable for use in contact with foodstuffs since it imparts no colour or taste to the products. It is also suitable for joinery and panelling.

Spruce, Black

Picea mariana

Black spruce is slow growing, reaching 15·3–18·3 m in height and 0·3 m in diameter. Its range is across Canada from the Atlantic coast to northern British Columbia and Alaska. It is one of the most northerly growing trees found on the tundra and extends south to northern Virginia and the Lake states. It forms vast areas of nearly pure forest and is the backbone of the huge pulp and paper industry in Canada.

The wood is similar in appearance to eastern Canadian spruce (*Picea glauca*) but is a little heavier, the seasoned timber weighing about 480 kg/m³ (30 lb/cu. ft). Its strength properties are similar to those of white spruce but it is rather stronger and harder. Kiln schedule K is recommended.

Apart from the main use for pulp, the timber is cut for mining props. Large trees are used for sawn timber, which is mixed with eastern Canadian spruce.

Spruce, Eastern Canadian

Picea glauca

Other names Canadian, Quebec, New Brunswick, St John, maritime spruce (Great Britain); northern, white, yellow spruce (Canada and USA); single, skunk, cat spruce (Canada).

The tree Eastern Canadian spruce grows to 36·6 m with a 1·2 m diameter on favourable sites but the average size is 24·4 m with a 0·6 m diameter. It ranges from Newfoundland to Alaska. With black spruce and tamarack larch it occurs at the northern limits of tree growth. Its southern extremities are Minnesota, Wisconsin and Michigan, eastwards to New York State.

The timber —general description An almost white to pale yellowish-brown lustrous wood, straight-grained, without appreciable odour, non-tainting and only slightly resinous, it closely resembles European spruce in appearance. Heartwood and sapwood are not visually distinct. The seasoned timber weighs about 420 kg/m³ (26 lb/cu. ft).

45

Seasoning	It is stated that the timber seasons fairly easily.

Kiln schedule K is recommended.

Shrinkage

Green to 12 per cent moisture content

Tangential	4 per cent
Radial	2 per cent

Mechanical properties	The strength properties of unseasoned timber of this species are in most cases practically identical with those of Canadian Sitka spruce, but its increase in strength as a result of seasoning is relatively rather less, and the air-dry timber is 15–20 per cent inferior in bending strength, stiffness, resistance to suddenly applied loads and to indentation. For structural purposes the timber is comparable with Baltic redwood of the same grade.
Resistance to insect attack	Logs are sometimes attacked by longhorn beetles, and there are a few records of damage by the beetle *Serropalpus barbatus* (Melandryidae), whose workings are indistinguishable from those of wood-wasps.
Natural durability	Non-durable.
Preservative treatment	Resistant.
Working properties	The timber works very easily in all hand and machine operations and has little dulling effect on cutting edges. Provided that sharp tools are used a clean finish can generally be obtained but the knots are apt to give trouble. It has good nailing and screwing properties, stains readily and takes paint, varnish, etc., well. Saw type C is recommended. The timber can be glued satisfactorily.
Uses	The timber when sawn is mixed with red and black spruce and Balsam fir and marketed as Canadian spruce. The timber is suitable for the same purposes as Baltic whitewood, such as general building, interior finishing, boxes and packing cases. Selected material is used in the musical instrument industry in the United States for soundboards, bars and key bottoms. It is extensively employed in eastern Canada for the manufacture of pulp and paper.

Spruce, Engelmann

Picea engelmannii

Other names	Mountain spruce and Rocky Mountain spruce (Canada and USA).
The tree	This species attains a height of 30·5–45·7 m and a diameter of 0·6–0·9 m. It is found on high mountain slopes in the west of North America, ranging from Alaska over the interior mountain system to the Sacramento Mountains in New Mexico and eastwards through Idaho and Montana to the eastern slopes of the Cascade Mountains in Oregon and Washington.
The timber —general description	The timber closely resembles that of the better known eastern Canadian spruce. Owing to the larger size of the trees there is a higher proportion of clear timber. The weight of the seasoned timber is about 430 kg/m³ (27 lb/cu. ft).
Seasoning	It is probable that this timber can be seasoned without difficulty and that there will be no serious degrade in the process.

Kiln schedule K is recommended.

Mechanical properties	The mechanical properties of Engelmann spruce appear to vary considerably with the locality of growth, timber from favourable sites in British Columbia being much denser and stronger than that from the lower Rocky Mountain region. Timber from British Columbia compares favourably with Sitka spruce, being 10–20 per cent softer and less resistant to impact, but very little different in other mechanical properties.

46

Resistance to insect attack	Logs are sometimes attacked by ambrosia (pinhole borer) beetles.
Natural durability	Non-durable.
Preservative treatment	Resistant.
Working properties	The timber works easily in all machine and hand operations and has little dulling effect on tools. It finishes cleanly but, as with most of the light, soft timbers, the use of sharp cutting edges is necessary to prevent tearing. The timber has good nailing properties and takes stain, paint and varnish well. Saw type C is recommended. The timber can be glued satisfactorily.
Veneer and plywood	Engelmann spruce is used in the western United States and Canada in the manufacture of plywood.
Uses	This wood is an important species in the interior of Canada and the United States. It is extensively employed for general building, carpentry and interior joinery. The lower grades are used for boxes and packing cases.

Spruce, European, or Whitewood[1]

Picea abies (*P. excelsa*)

Other names	White deal, common or Norway spruce, Baltic, Finnish, Russian whitewood, etc., according to place of origin (Great Britain).
The tree	The tree reaches an average height of 36·6 m with a 0·76–1·2 m diameter. It grows to its largest sizes in the Carpathian Mountains in Roumania where it attains a height of 61 m with a 1·5–1·8 m diameter. It is a native of Europe, extending from latitude 69° southwards to the Pyrenees, Alps and Carpathian Mountains and westwards into western Russia. In Great Britain it grows well on the hilly slopes of the west side of the country. The tree is naturally found in mountainous areas or in northern climates where there is no competition from the faster-growing hardwoods.
The timber —general description	The timber varies from almost white to pale yellowish-brown and has a natural lustre. The annual rings, marked by the contrast between the light springwood and darker summerwood, are less prominent than in Baltic redwood, and heartwood is lacking. Resin is present but is generally unobtrusive. The timber from the Baltic has an average weight of about 470 kg/m³ (29 lb/cu. ft), seasoned. Home-grown spruce is of faster growth and is slightly lighter in weight than this, while there is some evidence that supplies from south-eastern Europe are lighter still; these shipments normally include a substantial proportion of silver fir (*Abies alba*).
Seasoning	This timber seasons rapidly and well with little tendency to split or check, but with some risk of distortion, more especially in young growth timber with pronounced spiral grain.
	Kiln schedule K is advised.

Shrinkage

Green to 12 per cent moisture content

Tangential	about 4 per cent
Radial	about 2 per cent

Movement

Moisture content in 90 per cent humidity	20 per cent
Moisture content in 60 per cent humidity	12 per cent
Corresponding tangential movement	2·1 per cent
Corresponding radial movement	1 per cent
Classification	medium movement

[1] It is usual practice to include silver fir (*Abies alba*) in shipments of whitewood from central and southern Europe.

Mechanical properties	The imported European spruce is similar to Baltic redwood in its strength properties. The timber grown in the United Kingdom is some 20 per cent inferior to redwood in practically all strength properties before seasoning, but after seasoning the differences in strength between the two are so small as to be negligible.
Resistance to insect attack	Damage by longhorn and ambrosia (pinhole borer) beetles and by Siricid wood-wasps is sometimes present. There are occasional records of damage by the beetle *Serropalpus barbatus* (Melandryidae), whose workings are indistinguishable from those of wood-wasps.
	Seasoned sapwood is susceptible to attack by the common furniture beetle.
Natural durability	Non-durable.
Preservative treatment	Resistant.
Working properties	The timber works easily by hand and machine tools and has little dulling effect on their cutting edges. It has similar working properties to those of Sitka spruce but in general cuts more cleanly. It finishes well in most operations provided that the cutters are sharp. The material takes nails satisfactorily, stains effectively and gives good results with varnish and paint. Saw type C is recommended. The timber can be glued satisfactorily.
Veneer and plywood	The timber is often used in conjunction with *Pinus sylvestris* in northern Europe for the manufacture of plywood.
Uses	The larger timber is used for general interior joinery and carpentry, boxes and crates, etc. The spruce from Central and Eastern Europe (called 'Roumanian pine' or 'Swiss pine') is considered the best for soundboards of pianos and for bellies of violins. Smaller trees are used in the round for scaffold and flag poles, masts and pitprops and for other similar purposes. It is extensively used for the manufacture of pulp and paper. In Germany the bark is stripped and used for tannin extraction.
	The quality of spruce depends on the district in which it is grown; generally, the farther north, the better the quality. Trees grown at the same latitude will produce different grades of timber according to the altitude and the density of the stand.
	Norway spruce grown in Great Britain produces good timber but seldom high-class joinery grades. It is suitable for interior building work, carcassing, flooring in domestic dwellings, carpentry, etc., and the small material is used for masts and pitprops.

Spruce, Red

Picea rubens

Red spruce attains a height of 18·3–24·4 m and a diameter of 0·3–0·6 m. The tree has a limited range on the Atlantic seaboard of Canada and the New England states, stretching inland through southern Quebec to eastern Ontario and northern Tennessee.

The timber is generally similar to eastern Canadian spruce (*Picea glauca*) but tends to have rather more distinct summerwood bands, giving the wood a rather more prominent figure. This feature is not sufficiently marked to permit the two timbers to be distinguished with any certainty. The seasoned timber weighs about 450 kg/m³ (28 lb/cu. ft).

The timber works very easily in all hand and machine operations and has little dulling effect on cutting edges. It is stated that it seasons fairly easily but shrinks considerably in drying. Kiln schedule K would appear to be suitable. The strength properties are similar to those of yellow pine (*Pinus strobus*). The timber is resistant to preservative treatment and is non-durable.

It is marketed mixed with eastern white spruce and balsam fir as Canadian spruce or eastern Canadian spruce. It is employed for general construction, carpentry, box-making, etc. When grown with black spruce it is used for pulp and paper-making.

Spruce, Sitka (Canada)

Picea sitchensis

Other names Silver spruce (Great Britain, Canada and USA); Menzies and coast spruce (Canada); tideland spruce (USA and Canada).

The tree The tree is usually from 38–53·4 m high with a diameter of 0·9–1·8 m above its strongly buttressed and much enlarged base, but occasionally reaches 76·3 m in height with a diameter of 2·4–3·7 m. It is found on the Pacific coast of North America from Kodiak Island, southward through British Columbia, Washington and into California, seldom extending inland more than 80 kilometres. It is most abundant in the Queen Charlotte Islands.

The timber —general description A high-class, light-weight, softwood timber of fairly uniform texture, resembling the soft white pines, e.g. Canadian yellow pine, in this respect. It is non-resinous, odourless and non-tainting. It is mostly straight-grained but spiral grain is sometimes present. Growth rate is variable but the bulk of imported material is of moderate to slow even growth. Sitka spruce differs from other spruce timbers in having a light pinkish-brown heartwood which, however, is not sharply defined from the paler-coloured wide sapwood. The timber weighs about 430 kg/m³ (27 lb/cu. ft), seasoned.

Seasoning The timber is not difficult to season, especially in boards or small scantlings, but care must be exercised in seasoning valuable, high-quality stock of large sizes. It air seasons and kiln seasons fairly rapidly and well although some warping, splitting and loosening of knots must be expected.

Kiln schedule J is advised.

Shrinkage

Green to 12 per cent moisture content
Tangential	5 per cent
Radial	3 per cent

Mechanical properties Sitka spruce is a light timber, the strength properties of which are high for its weight. It is partly by virtue of this high strength-weight ratio that the prime timber has been used so extensively for aircraft purposes. Compared with Baltic redwood the seasoned timber is about 10 per cent lighter, 25 per cent stiffer and equal in bending strength, hardness and resistance to splitting.

Resistance to insect attack Logs are sometimes attacked by ambrosia (pinhole borer) beetles, and there are records of damage by the jewel beetle, *Buprestis aurulenta* (Buprestidae).

Natural durability Non-durable.

Preservative treatment Resistant.

Working properties The timber works easily in all hand and machine operations and has little dulling effect on cutting edges. It is generally slightly tougher and superior in quality and straightness of grain to the better grades of eastern Canadian spruce. A clean finish is obtained in machining provided that sharp tools are used. The timber takes nails and screws well, stains readily and gives good results with the various finishing treatments when normal care is taken to prevent grain raising. Saw type C is recommended. The timber can be glued satisfactorily.

Veneer and plywood It is seldom used for ordinary plywood, but sliced veneers are employed in special laminates for aircraft.

Uses The tree is large and produces a high proportion of defect-free timber. Owing to its high strength for its weight it is used specially for aeroplane and glider construction, oars, and the building of boats, particularly racing sculls; it is also employed for sound-boards in piano manufacture. In Canada it is used for interior joinery, building, cooperage, box-making, paper-pulp, etc.

49

Spruce, Sitka (Great Britain)

Picea sitchensis

The tree The tree was introduced from western Canada in 1832 but extensive plantings were not made until after the First World War. It is planted mainly in the west of England and Scotland and throughout Wales. It does not seem that the tree will grow to the height and size to which it grows in Canada, but quality Class I plantations reach a height of 33·6 m and a diameter of 0·6–0·9 m in 50 years. Owing to the extensive planting of the tree since the First World War, this species has become one of the main conifer species of the United Kingdom. The following information has been obtained mainly from plantation thinnings of up to 50 years old.

The timber —general description The bulk of the Sitka spruce produced in this country is of fast growth and consequently light in weight and coarse in texture: it hardly bears comparison with the select high-quality imported product. The seasoned timber weighs about 400 kg/m³ (25 lb/cu. ft), and green timber about 580 kg/m³ (36 lb/cu. ft) (80 per cent moisture content).

Seasoning The timber seasons rapidly and well though some warping, splitting and loosening of knots must be expected.

The material exhibits a greater tendency than the imported timber to collapse during drying and to warp, especially in the form of twist and cup. There is a wide variation both in the freedom with which the timber parts with its moisture and in its liability to collapse.

Kiln schedule J is advised.

Shrinkage

Green to 12 per cent moisture content

Tangential	5 per cent
Radial	3 per cent

Movement

Moisture content in 90 per cent humidity	19 per cent
Moisture content in 60 per cent humidity	12·5 per cent
Corresponding tangential movement	1·3 per cent
Corresponding radial movement	0·9 per cent
Classification	small movement

Mechanical properties This is a light timber, the strength properties of which are high for its weight. Compared with Baltic redwood the seasoned timber is about 15–20 per cent lighter, 20 per cent lower in stiffness, and the best of the timber equal in bending strength, hardness and resistance to splitting.

Resistance to insect attack There are a few records of damage to logs by *Sirex* wood-wasps and the beetle *Hylecoetus dermestoides* (Lymexylidae).

Natural durability Non-durable.

Preservative treatment Resistant.

Working properties Although knots are inclined to be troublesome, the timber works easily with machine and hand tools. Unless very sharp tools are employed the broad bands of soft spring-wood do not cut cleanly and often tear in sawing and planing under normal conditions of working. The wood also tends to crumble when cut on end-grain with a chisel and, in comparison with imported material, gives a poor finish in most machine and hand operations. It takes nails well. Saw type C is recommended.

Uses The timber varies considerably in strength according to the locality in which it is grown. When machine graded, home-grown Sitka spruce gives a high yield of timber suitable for structural purposes. Other uses are boxes, packing cases, pallets, sheds, agricultural buildings, etc. The timber makes good pulp for paper and can be used for the manufacture of wood wool.

Spruce, Western White

Picea glauca var. *albertiana*

The tree Western white spruce attains a height of 48·8 m and a diameter of 0·9–1·2 m. It resembles Engelmann spruce (*Picea engelmannii*) and it is difficult to separate the species without the cones. The tree grows from Manitoba westward almost to the Pacific coast and northwards into Alaska. It spreads southwards on the western slopes of the Rocky Mountains into the United States.

The timber —general description Western white spruce differs from the eastern variety in that it has a finer and more even texture and is relatively more free from defects, features attributable to the large size of the tree and its conditions of growth.

Seasoning This timber can probably be seasoned with little degrade.

Kiln schedule K is suggested.

Mechanical properties The strength properties of the unseasoned timber are practically identical with those of Sitka spruce, but its increase in strength as a result of seasoning is relatively rather less and the air-dry timber is 15–20 per cent inferior in bending strength, stiffness, resistance to suddenly applied loads and to indentation. For structural purposes the timber is comparable with Baltic redwood of the same grade.

Resistance to insect attack Logs are sometimes attacked by ambrosia (pinhole borer) beetles.

Natural durability Non-durable.

Working properties The timber works very easily in all hand and machine operations and has little dulling effect on cutting edges. Provided that sharp tools are used, a clean finish can generally be obtained but the knots are apt to give trouble. It has good nailing and screwing properties, stains readily and takes paint, varnish, etc., well. Saw type C is recommended. The timber can be glued satisfactorily.

Veneer and plywood The timber is used in the western United States and Canada for the manufacture of veneers or plywood.

Uses It is used extensively and is an important species in Canada for joinery, building and general construction. It is imported into Great Britain as an individual species and, owing to its greater widths and lengths than whitewood from the Baltic, it is used for special purposes such as scaffold planks and work needing greater dimensions than those readily obtained from the Scandinavian countries. It has a high potential value in western Canada for pulp. A percentage of this timber is sometimes mixed with western hemlock and sold under the latter name.

Totara

Podocarpus totara and *P. hallii*

The tree A medium to large tree, sometimes attaining a height of 39·6 m, although the average height at maturity is probably about 21·4 m; diameter 0·6–1·5 m. Merchantable boles of *P. totara* vary in length from 9·5 to 24·4 m and of *P. hallii* from 7·3 to 18·3 m. *P. totara* is found in both lowland and mountain forests in the North and South Islands of New Zealand. *P. hallii* also occurs in Stewart Island.

The timber —general description Totara is a straight-grained softwood, medium reddish-brown in colour. As in other softwoods of the southern hemisphere, growth rings are not clearly defined. The timber has a fairly fine, even texture unlike that of a typical European softwood. Its weight, in the seasoned condition, is about 480 kg/m³ (30 lb/cu. ft).

Seasoning The timber is stated to season quickly and well. It is reputed to be very stable in use after suitable seasoning.

Kiln schedule J is recommended.

51

Mechanical properties	For its weight, totara is comparatively weak in static bending, especially after seasoning. Thus, although the air-dry timber is about as heavy and as hard as Baltic redwood, its bending strength and stiffness are some 25–30 per cent lower, and although figures are not available it is stated also to have low shock resistance in bending. Its compressive strength, about 15 per cent below that of Baltic redwood, is relatively better than its bending strength, and for this reason totara is more suited for use as columns and posts than as beams or joists.
Resistance to insect attack	Seasoned timber is recorded in New Zealand as liable to attack by the common furniture beetle.
Natural durability	Durable.
Preservative treatment	Resistant. The sapwood is permeable.
Working properties	The timber works readily in all hand and machine operations. It turns well and machines to a good clean finish provided that sharp cutters are employed, but care is needed to prevent breaking away at the exit of the tool when cutting across the grain. *P. hallii* tends to be interlocked in grain and is reported to be much more difficult to split and machine than *P. totara*. The timber is reported to hold nails and screws well but to require special treatment in painting owing to the presence of resin. Saw type D is recommended.
Uses	Although no timber is immune from attack by marine borers, totara is the only softwood generally recognised as being resistant to attack, making it suitable for dock and sea work. In New Zealand it is employed for bridges, and wharf and ship building. It is suitable for flooring, exterior joinery work and work in contact with the ground.

'Western Red Cedar'

Thuja plicata

Other names	'British Columbia red cedar' (Great Britain); 'red cedar' (Canada); giant arborvitae (USA).
The tree	'Western red cedar' grows to a height of 45·7–76·3 m with a diameter of 0·9–2·4 m. It ranges from Alaska southwards to California, extending eastward along many of the interior ranges of British Columbia, northern Washington, Idaho and Montana, to the western slope of the continental divide. It has been planted to some extent in Great Britain, where it grows well, and it is also grown in limited quantities in New Zealand.
The timber —general description	A reddish-brown, non-resinous, light-weight softwood, straight-grained, somewhat coarse in texture and with a fairly prominent growth-ring figure. The timber weighs about 370 kg/m³ (23 lb/cu. ft), seasoned. The heartwood, which is quite distinct from the narrow, white sapwood, shows considerable colour variation when fresh, from dark chocolate-brown to a salmon colour. The darker material is mostly from the centre of the log and the brighter-coloured wood from near the outside, but alternate light and dark zones also occur. In technical properties the differently coloured heartwood zones are similar and on exposure the lighter colours rapidly tone down to a uniform russet- or reddish-brown while timber exposed to the weather assumes a silver-grey colour.
Seasoning	The timber seasons readily in the thinner dimensions with very little degrade, but some planks may prove very difficult to dry in the thicker sizes. In attempting to extract the moisture from the centre of such thick material, severe collapse accompanied by honeycombing may occur. Home-grown timber of this species appears generally to be rather more prone to collapse.
	Kiln schedule J is recommended.

Shrinkage
Green to 12 per cent moisture content

Tangential	2·5 per cent
Radial	1·5 per cent

52

Movement

Imported material

Moisture content in 90 per cent humidity	14 per cent
Moisture content in 60 per cent humidity	9·5 per cent
Corresponding tangential movement	0·9 per cent
Corresponding radial movement	0·4 per cent
Classification	small movement

Home-grown material

Moisture content in 90 per cent humidity	21 per cent
Moisture content in 60 per cent humidity	13 per cent
Corresponding tangential movement	1·9 per cent
Corresponding radial movement	0·8 per cent
Classification	small movement

Mechanical properties   A soft, light timber of correspondingly low strength properties. When air-dry, it is about 15 per cent less stiff than Baltic redwood, and 20–30 per cent inferior in bending strength, in resistance to suddenly applied loads and in crushing strength along the grain. Its resistance to splitting and indentation (on the side grain) is about 40 per cent below that of Baltic redwood.

Resistance to insect attack   Standing trees are liable to infestation by the Western cedar borer *Trachykele blondeli* (Buprestidae). Seasoned timber is not immune from attack by furniture beetles.

The timber is resistant but not immune from damage by termites, the powers of resistance varying according to the species of termite.

Natural durability   Durable.

Preservative treatment   Resistant.

Working properties   The timber works easily in all hand and machine operations and has little dulling effect on tools. A good finish is generally obtainable, provided that sharp cutters are used. It has a somewhat brittle nature and may splinter to a certain extent when worked on end-grain, as in mortising, end moulding, etc. In planing and moulding, particularly of fast-grown material, dulled or thickened cutters tend to compress the soft spring-wood, which later expands and produces ridged surfaces. 'Western red cedar' belongs to the class of timbers that is subject to chip-bruising under certain machining con-ditions. This difficulty can generally be overcome by improving the efficiency of the waste-removal system and by having the cutters free of all wire-edge. The timber has fairly good nailing properties but hot-dipped galvanised or copper nails should be used; it screws well and takes stain and paint satisfactorily.

Timber grown in Great Britain contains frequent small knots, which are liable to cause tearing in planing and moulding, but, in general, its working properties are similar to those of fast-grown imported material. The wide bands of soft springwood are rather troublesome in end-grain working, especially with the chisel, for they tend to crumble under the tools. The knots sometimes interfere with the cutting action of hand tools but they present no difficulty in machining operations. Saw type C is recommended.

Uses   The sawn timber is used where light weight and durability are required, such as in glass-house construction. It is employed in the production of shingles, interior finishing and exterior work such as timber boarding and for outhouses. It is considered a very suitable timber for the construction of beehives.

The timber has acidic properties and tends to accelerate the corrosion of metals in contact with it: e.g. in contact with unprotected iron the wood develops a black stain and the iron corrodes. Suitable precautions should be taken, either by applying protective coatings to the metals in contact with the wood, or by choice of metals which are relatively resistant to corrosion. Because of these properties the timber should not be used for cable drums, troughs for cables, cases for metal goods, etc.

53

'White Cedar'

Thuja occidentalis

'White cedar' is also called 'northern white cedar' or 'eastern white cedar' and eastern arborvitae. It grows to a height of 15·3–18·3 m and a diameter of 0·6–0·9 m, and is found in North America from Nova Scotia to Manitoba, its northern limits being James Bay and its southern extremity Minnesota and the mountains of Virginia. It often forms pure stands in swampy areas and is also found mixed with black spruce.

The timber is light in weight (about 340 kg/m³ (21 lb/cu. ft), seasoned), durable, comparable to 'western red cedar' in character but, unlike the latter, generally available only in comparatively small dimensions. It is pale brown in colour with narrow and rather inconspicuous summerwood bands. The seasoned timber retains a faint spicy odour. It is resistant or extremely resistant to preservative impregnation and the sapwood is also resistant. 'White cedar', being light in weight, has correspondingly low strength properties. It is much less stiff than 'western red cedar' but has appreciably greater toughness and shock resistance. Kiln schedule J is recommended.

Owing to its durability it is used in America for work where it is in contact with the ground or exposed to weather, such as fence posts, rails, sleepers and shingles.

'Yellow Cedar'

Chamaecyparis nootkatensis

Other names	'Alaska yellow cedar', nootka false cypress (USA); yellow cypress (Canada).
The tree	'Yellow cedar' grows to a height of 24·4 m with a diameter of 0·6–0·9 m and a sharply tapering bole. The tree is confined to the Pacific coast area from Alaska south to southern Oregon. It is most abundant and largest in size in Alaska and northern British Columbia.
The timber —general description	This is a pale yellow wood of fine even texture. The dry timber has no appreciable odour and differs in this respect from the related 'Port Orford cedar' (*Chamaecyparis lawsoniana*), which has a persistent spicy and fragrant odour. The seasoned timber weighs about 500 kg/m³ (31 lb/cu. ft).
Seasoning	No information from tests is available. It probably seasons with little degrade from warping, as the timber is stated to have very low shrinkage factors. Kiln schedule J is suggested as likely to be suitable.
Mechanical properties	No strength data on this species grown in Canada are available. The results of tests made in the United States on timber from Alaska and from Oregon showed the air-dry timber to be, on the average, about 25 per cent less resistant to splitting than Baltic redwood, but otherwise of about the same strength as that timber. The material from trees grown in Alaska was appreciably heavier and generally stronger than that from trees grown in Oregon.
Wood bending properties	No exact data are available on the limiting radii of curvature of this species. Limited tests have, however, indicated that it cannot be bent to any appreciable extent without severe buckling and fibre rupture occurring. It appears generally to be unsuitable for solid bending purposes.
Resistance to insect attack	It is recorded as being susceptible to attack by drywood termites in the West Indies.
Natural durability	Durable.
Preservative treatment	Resistant.
Working properties	The working properties are similar to those of 'Port Orford cedar'. The timber converts cleanly and with ease. It works readily by hand and machine tools, has a very slight

54

dulling effect on their cutting edges and usually finishes excellently. Where the grain is wavy there is a slight tendency to pick up in planing and moulding. It takes nails well and stains, paints and varnishes satisfactorily. Saw type C or D is recommended. The timber can be glued satisfactorily.

Uses It is used locally for poles, piles, boat building, interior finishing in houses and furniture. A small quantity is exported and among its many uses it is considered to be one of the best woods for battery separators.

Yellowwood, British Honduras

Podocarpus guatemalensis

In British Honduras the timber is also called 'cypress'. The tree reaches a height of 9·2–18·3 m, with a diameter of up to 0·6 m. It is a tree of the hills and mountain forests in the southern half of British Honduras and in Guatemala and has been recorded in southern Mexico. The timber closely resembles that of podo from East Africa. Strength tests at the Laboratory on a limited quantity of this timber suggest that its strength properties resemble very closely those of the *Podocarpus* species of East Africa.

The timber appears to season at a moderate rate with some inclination to split and check, but with little inclination to warp.

Kiln schedule H is advised.

Shrinkage

Green to 12 per cent moisture content
Tangential	3·5 per cent
Radial	2 per cent

Movement

Moisture content in 90 per cent humidity	19 per cent
Moisture content in 60 per cent humidity	13 per cent
Corresponding tangential movement	1·7 per cent
Corresponding radial movement	0·9 per cent
Classification	small movement

The timber is moderately durable and is permeable to preservatives.

No exact data are available on the limiting radii of curvature of this species. Limited tests have, however, indicated that it cannot be bent to any appreciable extent without severe buckling and fibre rupture occurring. It appears generally to be unsuitable for solid bending purposes.

The timber is used locally for house construction, internal and external joinery and general purposes where strength is not a primary factor.

Yew

Taxus baccata

Other names Common or European yew (Great Britain).

The tree Yew grows to 12·2–15·3 m with a short bole which is generally more or less fluted and often consists of several vertical shoots which have fused. The tree grows longer and straighter in the south of Europe but never produces a clean long bole. It occurs throughout Europe from Scandinavia to the Mediterranean and from the Atlantic to the western provinces of Russia. It also occurs in Algeria, Asia Minor, the Caucasus, northern Iran, the Himalayas and Burma.

The timber
—general description The irregular habit of growth referred to above results in much of the timber having an irregular growth-ring figure, which is often of decorative value. The annual rings, which are clearly demarcated by a narrow zone of dense summerwood, show considerable variation in width even in different parts of the same ring; rings exceeding 0·254 cm ($\frac{1}{10}$ in.) are quite common and represent a rate of growth in diameter much

55

more rapid than is usually regarded as typical of yew. The heartwood varies in colour from orange-brown to dark purplish-brown; lighter-coloured wood often shows darker streaks. The extremely narrow sapwood is almost white in colour and is sharply demarcated. Yew is the heaviest of the softwood timbers, apart from the denser types of pitch pine, averaging 670 kg/m³ (42 lb/cu. ft) when seasoned and about 1120 kg/m³ (70 lb/cu. ft), green (100 per cent moisture content).

Seasoning — This timber seasons well and fairly rapidly. Existing shakes tend to open but distortion is negligible.

Kiln schedule G is recommended.

Shrinkage

Green to 12 per cent moisture content
Tangential	3·5 per cent
Radial	2 per cent

Mechanical properties — Only a very limited number of strength tests have been made on yew at the Laboratory, and numerical comparison can be made, therefore, for only a few of its mechanical properties. It is a hard timber, its resistance to indentation being practically equal to that of oak. Its compressive strength along the grain is also very high for a softwood, again being equal to that of oak. In its resistance to splitting, straight-grained timber is about 20 per cent inferior to oak. It is considered to be a tough, resilient timber, but no numerical data are available for these properties.

Wood bending properties — This species is one of the best softwoods for solid bending purposes. Knots have little effect but the wood is inclined to check during the drying and setting process. The use of straight-grained and air-dried timber is to be advocated.

Classification	good
For solid bends (*steamed*)	
R/S (supported)	8·5
R/S (unsupported)	16·5
For thin laminae (*unsteamed*)	
R/S	54

Resistance to insect attack — The timber is not immune from attack by the common furniture beetle.

Natural durability — Durable.

Preservative treatment — Resistant.

Working properties — Straight-grained material works to a good finish in most operations, but when curly-grain or cross-grain is present pronounced tearing may occur in planing and moulding. When this occurs a reduction in cutting angle to 15° or less is needed to produce clean surfaces. The timber cuts moderately readily by hand and machine tools. It turns excellently, gives good results with stain and takes a high polish. Saw type E is recommended. The timber can be glued satisfactorily but care is necessary because of the oily nature of the wood.

Veneer and plywood — Yew makes a pleasant decorative veneer.

Uses — The timber is difficult to obtain in large clean planks owing to the form of growth. It is a good wood for turning and for decorative work. Owing to its durability it is used for fence and gate posts and other work where the timber is in contact with the ground.

Appendix I

Types of saws

Specifications for the spring-set teeth of circular saws for ripsawing various timbers, including those described in the handbook, for a rim speed of 9000–10 000 ft/min.

Type	Class of timber	No of teeth	Pitch (in.)	Hook Green material	Hook Seasoned material	Clearance	Top bevel	Depth of gullet (in.)
A	Hardwoods of abrasive nature, e.g. teak, 'Queensland walnut'	32 40	0·0982 × dia. 0·0785 × dia.	20°/25°	15°/20°	15°	10°	0·35 × pitch
B	Hardwoods of 'fibrous' nature and for fast sawing of milder hard- woods, e.g. gurjun	40 46	0·0785 × dia. 0·0683 × dia.	20°	15°	20°	15°	0·4 × pitch
C	Softwoods, lighter classes, and for fast sawing, e.g. spruce, Parana pine	46	0·0683 × dia.	25°/30°	25°	20°	15°	0·45 × pitch
D	Softwoods, heavier classes, and for better sawn finish, e.g. larch, pitch pine	54	0·0582 × dia.	25°	25°	20°	15°	0·45 × pitch
E	Hardwoods, low to medium density, e.g. mahogany, birch, beech	54	0·0582 × dia.	25°	20°	15°	15°	0·4 × pitch
F	Hardwoods, medium to higher density, e.g. dense oak, jarrah	60 66	0·523 × dia. 0·0477 × dia.	20°	15°	15°	10°	0·4 × pitch
G	Dense hardwoods, e.g. ebony	80	0·0393 × dia.	10°	10°	15°	5°	0·4 × pitch

Note. For purposes of simplicity the general run of hardwoods in this table has been classified into only three density groups (see Types E, F and G).

The tooth pitch of saw types A and B should not greatly exceed 3 in. if moderately fast feeds are required. The choice of the number of teeth will depend therefore on the diameter of the saw. In the case of saw type F, the larger number of teeth should be used for denser timber.

For further information relating to tooth shapes, sizes, etc., see *A Handbook of Woodcutting* and *Mechanics of Sawing: Band and Circular Saws* (Forest Products Research Bulletin, No. 30), published by HMSO.

Appendix II

Kiln schedules

It must be emphasised that these schedules are subject to revision and are approximate only, representing conditions suitable for average qualities of timber intended for normal use. Experience with timber from particular sources of supply destined for specific purposes will generally enable modifications to be made. Such modifications may indeed often prove to be very pronounced since, for example, good quality small dimension material will almost always be found to tolerate appreciably severer drying conditions than through and through planks from poorer quality wood of the same species.

These schedules are designed for use with timbers up to about 3·81 cm (1½ in.) thick, dried in a forced draught kiln. Thicker dimensions require somewhat higher humidities to prevent severe moisture gradients from developing. When drying timber between 3·81 cm (1½ in.) and 7·62 cm (3 in.) thick, the relative humidity should be 5 per cent higher at each stage of the appropriate schedule, and 10 per cent higher with wood greater than 7·62 cm (3 in.) in thickness.

Kiln schedule A Suitable for timbers which must not darken in drying and for those which have a pronounced tendency to warp but are not particularly liable to check.

Moisture content (%) of the wettest timber on the air-inlet side at which changes are to be made	Temperature (Dry bulb)		Temperature (Wet bulb)		Relative humidity % (approx)
	°F	°C	°F	°C	
Green	95	35	87	30·5	70
60	95	35	83	28·5	60
40	100	38	84	29	50
30	110	43·5	88	31·5	40
20	120	48·5	92	34	35
15	140	60	105	40·5	30

Kiln schedule B Suitable for timbers that are very prone to check.

Moisture content (%) of the wettest timber on the air-inlet side at which changes are to be made	Temperature (Dry bulb)		Temperature (Wet bulb)		Relative humidity % (approx)
	°F	°C	°F	°C	
Green	105	40·5	101	38	85
40	105	40·5	99	37	80
30	110	43·5	102	39	75
25	115	46	105	40·5	70
20	130	54·5	115	46	60
15	140	60	118	47·5	50

Kiln schedule C

Moisture content (%) of the wettest timber on the air-inlet side at which changes are to be made	Temperature (Dry bulb)		Temperature (Wet bulb)		Relative humidity % (approx)
	°F	°C	°F	°C	
Green	105	40·5	101	38	85
60	105	40·5	99	37	80
40	110	43·5	102	39	75
35	110	43·5	100	38	70
30	115	46	103	39·5	65
25	125	51·5	109	43	60
20	140	60	118	47·5	50
15	150	65·5	121	49	40

Kiln schedule D

Moisture content (%) of the wettest timber on the air-inlet side at which changes are to be made	Temperature (Dry bulb)		Temperature (Wet bulb)		Relative humidity % (approx)
	°F	°C	°F	°C	
Green	105	40·5	101	38	85
60	105	40·5	99	37	80
40	105	40·5	96	35·5	70
35	110	43·5	97	36	60
30	115	46	97	36	50
25	125	51·5	101	38	40
20	140	60	105	40·5	30
15	150	65·5	112	44·5	30

Kiln schedule E

Moisture content (%) of the wettest timber on the air-inlet side at which changes are to be made	Temperature (Dry bulb)		Temperature (Wet bulb)		Relative humidity % (approx)
	°F	°C	°F	°C	
Green	120	48·5	115	46	85
60	120	48·5	113	45	80
40	125	51·5	116	46·5	75
30	130	54·5	117	47	65
25	140	60	120	49	55
20	155	68	127	53	45
15	170	76·5	136	58	40

Kiln schedule F

Moisture content (%) of the wettest timber on the air-inlet side at which changes are to be made	Temperature (Dry bulb)		Temperature (Wet bulb)		Relative humidity % (approx)
	°F	°C	°F	°C	
Green	120	48·5	111	44	75
60	120	48·5	109	43	70
40	125	51·5	109	43	60
30	130	54·5	109	43	50
25	140	60	115	46	45
20	155	68	124	51	40
15	170	76·5	136	58	40

Kiln schedule G

Suitable for timbers which dry very slowly, but which are not particularly prone to warp.

Moisture content (%) of the wettest timber on the air-inlet side at which changes are to be made	Temperature (Dry bulb)		Temperature (Wet bulb)		Relative humidity % (approx)
	°F	°C	°F	°C	
Green	120	48·5	115	46	85
60	120	48·5	113	45	80
40	130	54·5	123	50·5	80
30	140	60	131	55	75
25	160	71	146	63·5	70
20	170	76·5	147	64	55
15	180	82	144	62·5	40

Kiln schedule H

Moisture content (%) of the wettest timber on the air-inlet side at which changes are to be made	Temperature (Dry bulb)		Temperature (Wet bulb)		Relative humidity % (approx)
	°F	°C	°F	°C	
Green	135	57	127	53	80
50	135	57	126	52	75
40	140	60	126	52	65
30	150	65·5	129	54	55
20	170	76·5	136	58	40

Kiln schedule J

Moisture content (%) of the wettest timber on the air-inlet side at which changes are to be made	Temperature (Dry bulb)		Temperature (Wet bulb)		Relative humidity % (approx)
	°F	°C	°F	°C	
Green	135	57	123	50·5	70
50	135	57	119	48	60
40	140	60	118	47·5	50
30	150	65·5	121	49	40
20	170	76·5	127	53	30

Kiln schedule K

Moisture content (%) of the wettest timber on the air-inlet side at which changes are to be made	Temperature (Dry bulb)		Temperature (Wet bulb)		Relative humidity % (approx)
	°F	°C	°F	°C	
Green	160	71	151	66	80
50	170	76·5	156	68·5	70
30	180	82	159	70·5	60
20	190	88	153	67·5	40

Kiln schedule L

Moisture content (%) of the wettest timber on the air-inlet side at which changes are to be made	Temperature (Dry bulb)		Temperature (Wet bulb)		Relative humidity % (approx)
	°F	°C	°F	°C	
Green	180	82	165	74	70
40	200	93·5	162	72	40

Kiln schedule M

Moisture content (%) of the wettest timber on the air-inlet side at which changes are to be made	Temperature (Dry bulb)		Temperature (Wet bulb)		Relative humidity % (approx)
	°F	°C	°F	°C	
Green	200	93·5	184	84·5	70
50	210	99	179	81·5	50

Index to the timbers

Names in bold type are standard names under which the timbers are arranged alphabetically in the text from pages 9 to 56

Printed in England for Her Majesty's Stationery Office
by The Campfield Press, St. Albans

(7864). Dd.699221. K.6. 1/81. Gp. 3319.